BOB DYLAN
BOOTLEG
SONGBOOK

BOB DYLAN BOOTLEG SONGBOOK

Wise Publications
part of The Music Sales Group
London/New York/Paris/Sydney/Copenhagen/Berlin/Madrid/Hong Kong/Tokyo

PUBLISHED BY
WISE PUBLICATIONS
14-15 BERNERS STREET, LONDON, W1T 3LJ
EXCLUSIVE DISTRIBUTORS:
MUSIC SALES LIMITED
DISTRIBUTION CENTRE, NEWMARKET ROAD,
BURY ST EDMUNDS, SUFFOLK, IP33 3YB, UK.
MUSIC SALES CORPORATION
180 MADISON AVENUE, 24TH FLOOR,
NEW YORK NY 10016, USA
MUSIC SALES PTY LIMITED
4TH FLOOR, LISGAR HOUSE, 30-32 CARRINGTON
STREET, SYDNEY, NSW 2000, AUSTRALIA

ORDER NO. AM1010009
ISBN: 978-1-78558-306-3

BOOK DESIGN BY **PEARCE MARCHBANK** RDI
TEXT BY **GRAHAM VICKERS**
MUSIC ARRANGED BY **ALISTAIR WATSON**
MUSIC PROCESSED BY **SARAH LOFTHOUSE**,
    SEL MUSIC ART LTD
MUSIC & TEXT EDITED BY **NAOMI COOK**
GUITAR CHORDS EDITED BY **JAMES WELLAND**

PRINTED IN THE EU

Bob Dylan was always an innovator.

New York's Greenwich Village folk scene of the early 1960s had several talented contenders for the role of breakthrough artist, and while some insiders thought Tom Paxton would be the one to make it big, Bob Dylan turned out to be the man whose highly original songs and distinctive image would emerge from The Gaslight Cafe and Gerde's Folk City to catch the imagination of the wider public. Acts like Peter, Paul and Mary and The Byrds took Dylan songs into the charts, even as the young man himself adopted a sceptical stance towards mass culture.

Accordingly hailed as an acoustic folk artist of principle, he promptly embraced electric rock and a career-long pattern was established: Dylan would innovate and then, just as people were getting used to what he was doing, he would do something else.

Bob Dylan was also a ground breaker, albeit unwittingly, in another department of the music industry: the bootleg record. *Great White Wonder* (GWW) was a 25-track double vinyl album released in July 1969 by two enterprising young Los Angelenos who had a cheerful disregard for legal niceties. It came in a featureless white sleeve on the obscure TMQ label and contained Dylan recordings obtained from various sources, including the famous *Basement Tapes* where he was accompanied by The Band, some recordings made in a Minnesota hotel room, and some studio outtakes. LA radio stations played them gleefully and GWW became an international phenomenon, much-copied tapes and pressings being sold in street markets, head shops and hippie emporia in LA, New York, Paris, London, Amsterdam and beyond. GWW was followed by more illegal Dylan compilations (*Stealin'*, *John Birch Society Blues*) and the bootleg record concept, hitherto a furtive phenomenon, now became high-profile as it gave access to intriguing examples of the mysterious Bob Dylan at play, off-guard or simply singing great self-penned songs of which you had never even heard.

The first release of bootlegged material was 1975's *The Basement Tapes*. In 1985, Dylan's official label,

Columbia, entered the fray with *Biograph*, a boxed set of five vinyl albums (or three CDs) containing 53 released and unreleased tracks from 1962 to 1981. Nowhere was the word 'bootleg' mentioned, but clearly those illegal Dylan records that had excited such fan interest were at last deemed worthy of a response from his record company. *Biograph* sold well and six years later Columbia launched its 'official' Dylan bootleg series, which was to become a rolling home for a wealth of rare, unreleased and newly-unearthed Dylan recordings, including some sparkling tracks that had made their lo-fi debut two decades earlier on GWW and its successors.

The sheer quantity of material in part reflects Dylan's characteristic impatience with his own songs, which more than once led him to abandon a potential classic for the want of a flawless take. There were other reasons, too, some of them discussed here in the accompanying song notes, which give details of how a song came about or why it remained unknown or forgotten until rediscovered and released anew.

This unique book contains specially-arranged versions of 36 Dylan performances drawn from several of those Columbia 'bootleg' volumes, *Biograph* and one or two other sources. The selection seeks to include some rare and little-heard songs as well as some live-performance variants of more familiar material, plus three of Dylan's most interesting songs for movies, otherwise available only on soundtrack albums.

The bootlegs have come full circle. If, in the digital download era, those original illegal bootleg pressings now sound like quaint relics of another age, their mission to release Dylan's undeservedly obscure work is now enshrined in Columbia's impressive ongoing bootleg series.

In that same spirit we are delighted to present these new arrangements of some truly fascinating Bob Dylan songs that, for a variety of reasons, fell between the cracks for a while, and then, happily, turned up again.

Graham Vickers

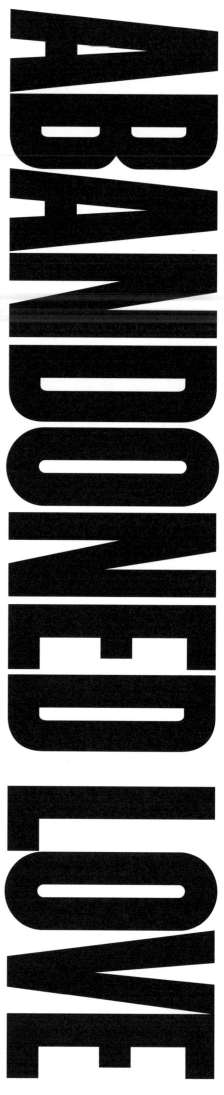

ABANDONED LOVE

RECORDED IN 1975
FIRST RELEASED IN 1985 ON
BIOGRAPH

Recorded on 31 July 1975, 'Abandoned Love' was originally intended for inclusion on *Desire*, one of Dylan's two indisputably great albums from the 1970s. There is something almost exultant about 'Abandoned Love', not just in Dylan's spirited vocal but also in the song's melodic construction. Far removed from *Desire's* raw and poignant 'Sara', 'Abandoned Love' is primarily an ebullient song about disenchantment. When it surfaced on *Biograph* in 1985, The Everly Brothers immediately covered it, as did George Harrison.

ABANDONED LOVE

WORDS & MUSIC BY BOB DYLAN
© COPYRIGHT 1975, RENEWED 2003 RAM'S HORN MUSIC.
ALL RIGHTS RESERVED. INTERNATIONAL COPYRIGHT SECURED.

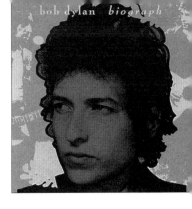

1. I can hear the turn-ing of ___ the key ___ I've been de-
(2.) pa - tron saint is a-fight-ing with a ghost ___ He's al-
(3.) come back to the town ___ from the flam-ing moon ___ I

(Verses 4-10 see block lyrics)

- ceived by the clown ___ in - side of me ___ I
- ways off ___ some - where when I need him most ___ The
see you in the streets, I be - gin to swoon ___ I

Verse 4:
Everybody's wearing a disguise
To hide what they've got left behind their eyes
But me, I can't cover what I am
Wherever the children go I'll follow them

Verse 5:
I march in the parade of liberty
But as long as I love you I'm not free
How long must I suffer such abuse
Won't you let me see you smile one time before I turn you loose?

Verse 6:
I've given up the game, I've got to leave
The pot of gold is only make-believe
The treasure can't be found by men who search
Whose gods are dead and whose queens are in the church

Verse 7:
We sat in an empty theater and we kissed
I asked ya please to cross me off-a your list
My head tells me it's time to make a change
But my heart is telling me I love ya but you're strange

Verse 8:
Instrumental

Verse 9:
One more time at midnight, near the wall
Take off your heavy makeup and your shawl
Won't you descend from the throne, from where you sit?
Let me feel your love one more time before I abandon it

Verse 10:
Instrumental

RECORDED IN 1962
FIRST RELEASED IN 1985 ON
BIOGRAPH

Recorded in New York City in 1962 as part of the *Freewheelin'* sessions, 'Baby, I'm In The Mood For You' sees Dylan in high spirits, his punchy lyrics flowing effortlessly over a chord progression borrowed from one-man-band Jesse Fuller's song 'San Francisco Bay Blues'. 'I'd done a few of his songs,' Dylan recalled, 'this was more'n likely my version of his thing.' The track remained unreleased until it was included on *Biograph*. In 1965, however, it was one of two comparatively obscure Dylan songs included on *Odetta Sings Dylan*, an entire album of covers by Odetta Holmes, the singer, actress, guitarist, songwriter and activist. To say she did the song justice is to damn with faint praise – hers is a simply wonderful rendition.

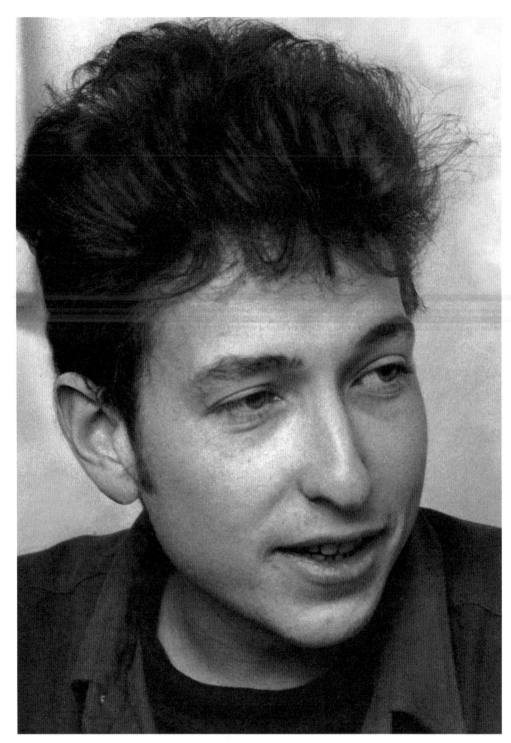

BABY, I'M IN THE MOOD FOR YOU

BABY, I'M IN THE MOOD FOR YOU

WORDS & MUSIC BY BOB DYLAN

1. Some-times I'm___ in the mood, I wan-na leave my lone-some home And
(*Verses 2-6 see block lyrics*)

some-times I'm___ in the mood, I wan-na hear my milk___ cow moan And

Oh babe, I'm in the mood for you.

Verse 2:
Sometimes I'm in the mood, Lord, I had my overflowin' fill
Sometimes I'm in the mood, I'm gonna make out my final will
Sometimes I'm in the mood, I'm gonna head for the walkin' hill
But then again, but then again, I said oh, I said oh, I said
Oh babe, I'm in the mood for you

Verse 3:
Sometimes I'm in the mood, I wanna lay right down and die
Sometimes I'm in the mood, I wanna climb up to the sky
Sometimes I'm in the mood, I'm gonna laugh until I cry
But then again, I said again, I said again, I said
Oh babe, I'm in the mood for you

Verse 4:
Sometimes I'm in the mood, I'm gonna sleep in my pony's stall
Sometimes I'm in the mood, I ain't gonna do nothin' at all
Sometimes I'm in the mood, I wanna fly like a cannonball
But then again, but then again, I said oh, I said oh, I said
Oh babe, I'm in the mood for you

Verse 5:
Sometimes I'm in the mood, I wanna back up against the wall
Sometimes I'm in the mood, I wanna run till I have to crawl
Sometimes I'm in the mood, I ain't gonna do nothin' at all
But then again, but then again, I said oh, I said oh, I said
Oh babe, I'm in the mood for you

Verse 6:
Sometimes I'm in the mood, I wanna change my house around
Sometimes I'm in the mood, I'm gonna make a change in this here town
Sometimes I'm in the mood, I'm gonna change the world around
But then again, but then again, I said oh, I said oh, I said
Oh babe, I'm in the mood for you

RECORDED IN 1983
(OUTTAKE FROM *INFIDELS*)
FIRST RELEASED IN 1991 ON
**THE BOOTLEG SERIES, VOLS 1-3:
RARE & UNRELEASED 1961-1991**

High up on the list of outtakes that everyone except Dylan seems to think should have been intakes, is 'Blind Willie McTell'. Omitted from *Infidels* because Dylan felt it never came out as he intended, it stands as the work of a mature songwriter. Had this been a 1960s Dylan paean to the legendary blues singer and guitarist from Georgia, it might have come out as a youthful homage, but 'Blind Willie McTell' was written by the 42-year-old Dylan and amounts to much more. Produced by Dylan and Mark Knopfler in New York City in May 1983, it is a desolate song of regret for the demise of all the genuine early twentieth century blues singers, first-hand witnesses to – and all too often victims of – disenfranchisement, pain and social injustice. It also seems to touch on the difficulties of living up to their legacy.

BLIND WILLIE McTELL

BLIND WILLIE McTELL

WORDS & MUSIC BY BOB DYLAN

Original key E♭ minor (Capo: Fret 1).

1. Seen the ar-row on___ the door-post___
(Verses 2-7 see block lyrics)

Say-ing___ "This land___ is con-demned___

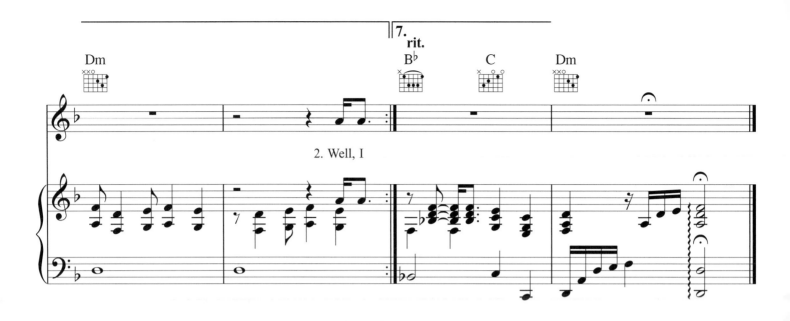

Verse 2:

Well, I heard that hoot owl singing
As they were taking down the tents
The stars above the barren trees
Were his only audience
Them charcoal gypsy maidens
Can strut their feathers well
But nobody can sing the blues
Like Blind Willie McTell

Verse 3:

See them big plantations burning
Hear the cracking of the whips
Smell that sweet magnolia blooming
See the ghosts of slavery ships
I can hear them tribes a-moaning
Hear the undertaker's bell
Nobody can sing the blues
Like Blind Willie McTell

Verse 4:

There's a woman by the river
With some fine young handsome man
He's dressed up like a squire
Bootlegged whiskey in his hand
There's a chain gang on the highway
I can hear them rebels yell
And I know no one can sing the blues
Like Blind Willie McTell

Verse 5:

Instrumental (until *)

𝄋 Verse 6:

Well, God is in His heaven
And we all want what's His
But power and greed and corruptible seed
Seem to be all that there is
I'm gazing out the window
Of the St. James Hotel
And I know no one can sing the blues
Like Blind Willie McTell

Verse 7:

Instrumental

CAN YOU PLEASE CRAWL OUT YOUR WINDOW?

RECORDED IN 1965
FIRST RELEASED IN 1985 ON
BIOGRAPH

Dylan notes that he was 'pressured into doing another single' in 1965. That single turned out to be this feisty pop song backed with 'Highway 61 Revisited' from the album of the same name on which the studio musicians were a group featuring Al Kooper and Michael Bloomfield. Various versions of 'Can You Please Crawl Out Your Window?' had been explored during the sessions for that album (these were released on Volume 12 of *The Bootleg Series*), but the eventual single was a different version again, this time with Robbie Robertson and The Hawks. It reached #58 on the US Billboard Hot 100 chart and #17 on the UK chart in January 1966, and was included on *Biograph*.

CAN YOU PLEASE CRAWL OUT YOUR WINDOW?

WORDS & MUSIC BY BOB DYLAN

1. He sits in___ your room, his tomb, with a fist full of tacks
(2.) looks_ so truth - ful,___ is this how he feels
(3.) looks so___ right - eous while_ your face is___ so changed

Pre - oc - cu - pied with his ven - geance
Try - ing to peel___ the moon_ and_ ex - pose it
Are___ you fright-ened of the box_ you_ keep___ him in

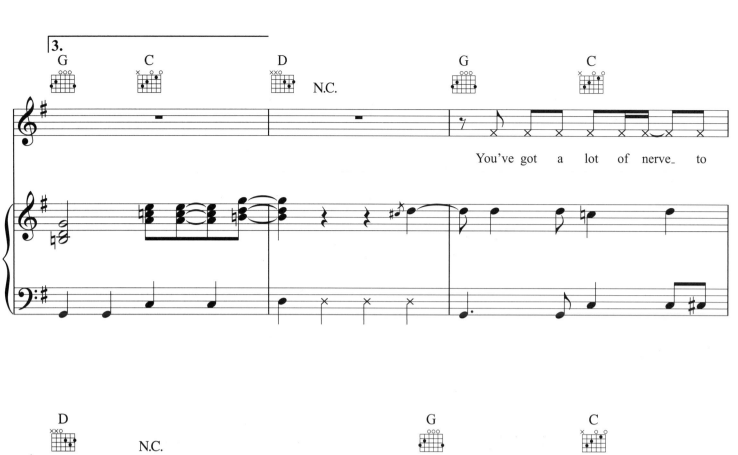

You've got a lot of nerve to

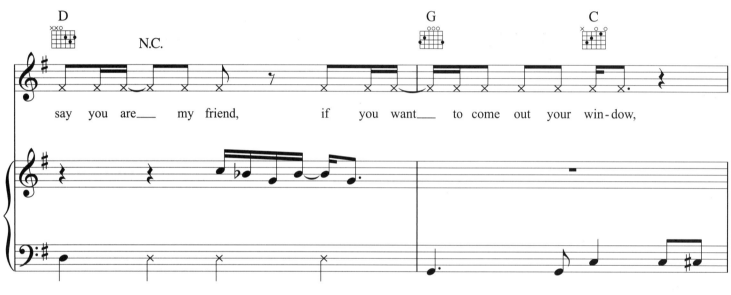

say you are___ my friend, if you want___ to come out your win-dow,

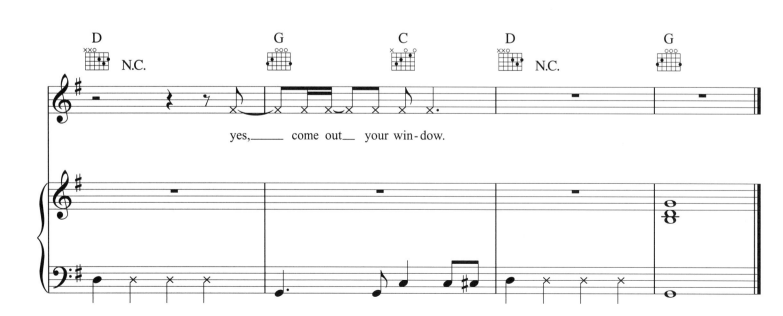

yes,___ come out___ your win-dow.

CARIBBEAN WIND

RECORDED IN 1981
FIRST RELEASED IN 1985 ON
BIOGRAPH

'Caribbean Wind' exists in several different incarnations but started life as a song intended for the album *Shot Of Love*, recorded at Rundown Studios in Santa Monica and Clover Studios in Hollywood during the spring of 1981. If some of Dylan's more opaque lyrics sometimes defy interpretation, 'Caribbean Wind' left even him baffled, not because of its narrative but for other reasons: 'That one I couldn't quite grasp what it was about after I finished it,' he said, 'sometimes you'll write something to be very inspired, and you won't quite finish it for one reason or another… then it's a struggle. The inspiration's gone and you can't remember why you started it in the first place. I think there's four different sets of lyrics to this. Maybe I got it right.'

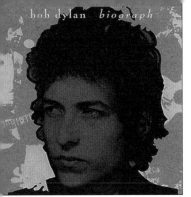

CARIBBEAN WIND

WORDS & MUSIC BY BOB DYLAN

1. She was the
rose of Sha-ron   from   pa - ra-dise_ lost   From the   ci - ty of   sev - en hills   near the
(3.) looked   in - to my soul through the   clothes that I   wore   She said, "We got a   mut - ual friend   o - ver
5. At-lan-tic Ci - ty   by the   cold   grey_ sea_   I hear a   voice cry-ing,_   "Dad-dy," I al-ways

RECORDED IN 2003
FIRST RELEASED IN 2003 ON
THE GODS AND GENERALS SOUNDTRACK ALBUM

Somehow Dylan's movie songs seem most at home in heroic historical settings. If *Pat Garrett and Billy The Kid* set the benchmark, *Gods and Generals* provided another sweeping tale of American history in the shape of the rise and fall of Thomas 'Stonewall' Jackson as he leads his Confederate forces against the Union. The movie was a pet project of CNN founder Ted Turner and won little critical or popular praise. Dylan's contribution is, however, memorable. ''Cross The Green Mountain' muses on the comradeship of battle and on the invisible forces sweeping the land. Contemplative and elegiac, it offers a song poem accompaniment (8 minutes long and complete with mournful fiddle) to director Ron Maxwell's very long (3 hours 39 minutes) and highly ambitious Civil War epic.

'CROSS THE GREEN MOUNTAIN

'CROSS THE GREEN MOUNTAIN

WORDS & MUSIC BY BOB DYLAN

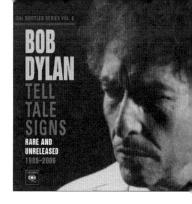

I crossed the green moun-tain, I slept by____ the stream

Hea-ven blaz-in' in my head, I dreamt a mon-strous dream____

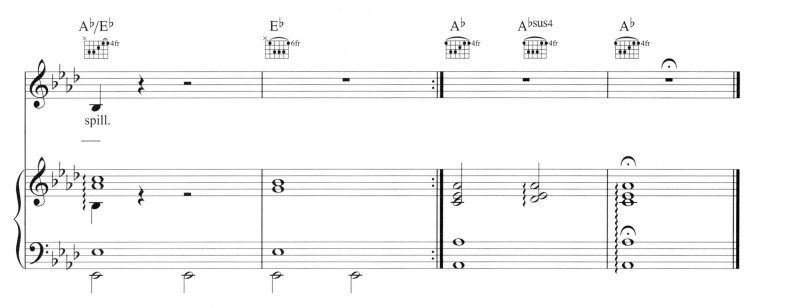

spill.

Additional lyrics:

Close the eyes of our Captain, peace may he know
His long night is done, the great leader is laid low
He was ready to fall, he was quick to defend
Killed outright he was by his own men

It's the last day's last hour of the last happy year
I feel that the unknown world is so near
Pride will vanish and glory will rot
But virtue lives and cannot be forgot

The bells of evening have rung
There's blasphemy on every tongue
Let them say that I walked in fair nature's light
And that I was loyal to truth and to right

Serve God and be cheerful, look upward beyond
Beyond the darkness that masks the surprises of dawn
In the deep green grasses of the blood stained wood
They never dreamed of surrendering. They fell where they stood

Stars fell over Alabama, I saw each star
You're walkin' in dreams whoever you are
Chilled are the skies, keen is the frost
The ground's froze hard and the morning is lost

A letter to mother came today
Gunshot wound to the breast is what it did say
But he'll be better soon he's in a hospital bed
But he'll never be better, he's already dead

I'm ten miles outside the city and I'm lifted away
In an ancient light that is not of day
They were calm, they were blunt, we knew 'em all too well
We loved each other more than we ever dared to tell

DIGNITY

RECORDED IN 1989
(DURING THE *OH MERCY* SESSIONS)
FIRST RELEASED IN 2008 ON
THE BOOTLEG SERIES, VOL. 8: TELL TALE SIGNS

First attempted in the spring of 1989 as part of the *Oh Mercy* studio sessions, this excellent song underwent a troubled recording history. An initial straightforward take produced an acceptable but unfinished result and producer Daniel Lanois wanted to try again using a Cajun band. This proved disastrous and eventually led to the song being excluded from the album. However, these versions were preceded by a piano demo, probably recorded in February of 1989, which was later included on a sampler as part of the promotional edition of Dylan's autobiographical *Chronicles: Volume One*. Along with a previously unreleased take of the song from the early *Oh Mercy* recording sessions, it also appeared on *The Bootleg Series, Vol. 8*, its calm and lyrical piano-led approach contrasting strikingly with its jauntier counterparts.

DIGNITY

WORDS & MUSIC BY BOB DYLAN

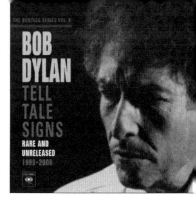

Fat man look-in' in a blade of steel_
(*See additional lyrics*)

Thin man look-in' at his last meal_

Hol-low man look-in' in a cot-ton-field For dig-ni-ty.___

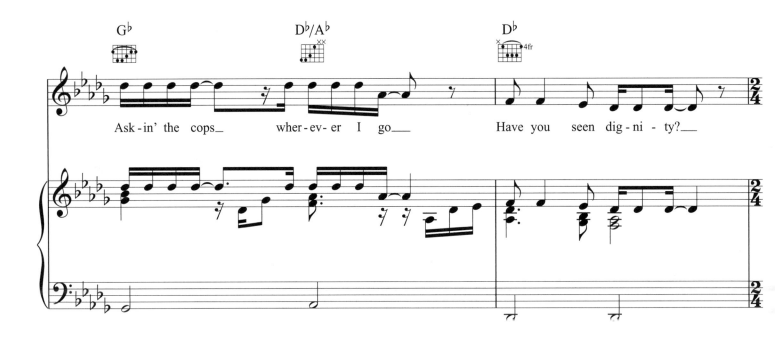

Ask-in' the cops___ wher-ev-er I go___ Have you seen dig-ni-ty?___

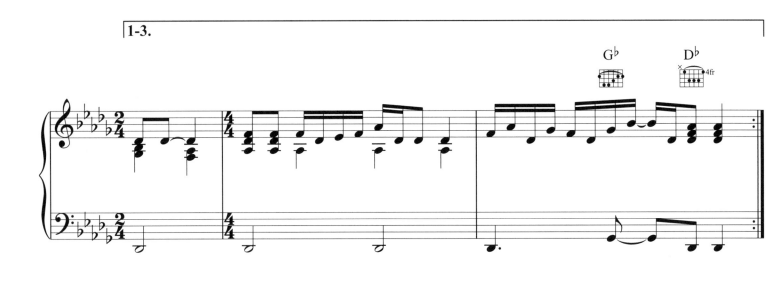

1-3.

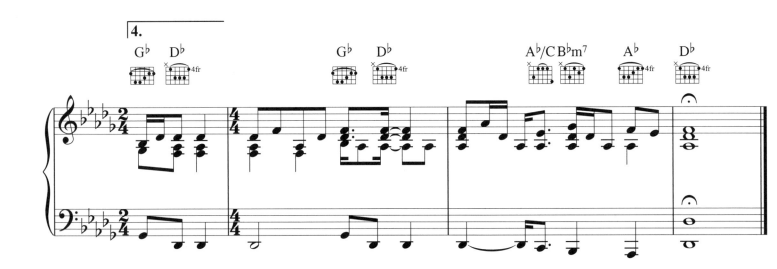

4.

Additional lyrics:
Blind man breakin' out of a trance
Puts both his hands in the pockets of chance
Hopin' to find one circumstance
Of dignity

I went to the wedding of Mary Lou
She said, "I don't want nobody see me talkin' to you"
Said she could get killed if she told me what she knew
About dignity

I went down where the vultures feed
I would've gone deeper, but there wasn't any need
Heard the tongues of angels and the tongues of men
Wasn't any difference to me

Chilly wind sharp as a razor blade
House on fire, debts unpaid
Gonna stand at the window, gonna ask the maid
Have you seen dignity?

Drinkin' man listens to the voice he hears
In a crowded room full of covered-up mirrors
Lookin' into the lost forgotten years
For dignity

Met Prince Phillip at the home of the blues
Said he'd give me information if his name wasn't used
He wanted money up front, said he was abused
By dignity

Footprints runnin' 'cross the silver sand
Steps goin' down into tattoo land
I met the sons of darkness and the sons of light
In the bordertowns of despair

Got no place to fade, got no coat
I'm on the rollin' river in a jerkin' boat
Tryin' to read a note somebody wrote
About dignity

Sick man lookin' for the doctor's cure
Lookin' at his hands for the lines that were
And into every masterpiece of literature
For dignity

Englishman stranded in the blackheart wind
Combin' his hair back, his future looks thin
Bites the bullet and he looks within
For dignity

Someone showed me a picture and I just laughed
Dignity never been photographed
I went into the red, went into the black
Into the valley of dry bone dreams

So many roads, so much at stake
So many dead ends, I'm at the edge of the lake
Sometimes I wonder what it's gonna take
To find dignity

DREAMIN' OF YOU

RECORDED IN 1997
(OUTTAKE FROM *TIME OUT OF MIND*)
FIRST RELEASED IN 2008 ON
THE BOOTLEG SERIES, VOL. 8: TELL TALE SIGNS

'Dreamin' of You' was recorded in January 1997 during the sessions for *Time Out Of Mind*, although it remained unreleased until 2008, when it was included on both *The Bootleg Series, Vol. 8* collection and released as a single. Additionally, a vinyl single version was provided with advance orders of *The Bootleg Series, Vol. 8*. The song has an uneasy, nightmarish quality and its edgy instrumentation supports a narrative of unrelieved despair focussed on the recurring couplet 'I've been dreamin' of you, that's all I do / And it's driving me insane.'

DREAMIN' OF YOU

WORDS & MUSIC BY BOB DYLAN
© COPYRIGHT 2008 SPECIAL RIDER MUSIC.
ALL RIGHTS RESERVED. INTERNATIONAL COPYRIGHT SECURED.

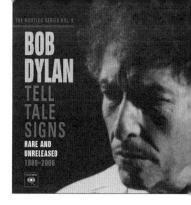

1. The light_ in this place
2. Some - where_ dawn is
3. May - be they'll get me,
(*Verses 4 & 5 see block lyrics*)

is real - ly bad___ Like be - ing at the bot - tom of a
break - ing Light is streak - ing 'cross the floor_
may - be they won't But what - ev - er it won't be to - night_

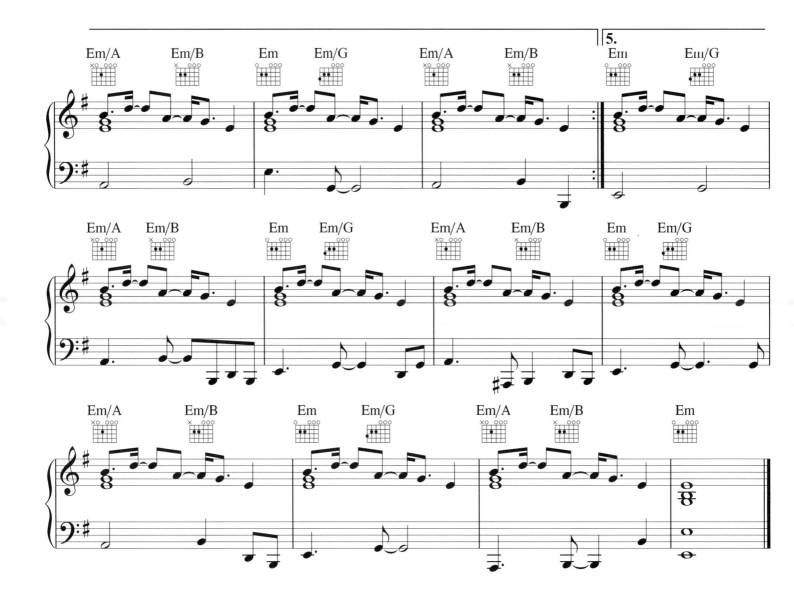

Verse 4:

Well, I eat when I'm hungry, drink when I'm dry

Live my life on the square

Even if the flesh falls off my face

It won't matter, long as you're there

Feel like a ghost in love

Underneath the heavens above

Feel further away than I ever did before

Feel further than I can take

Dreamin' of you is all I do

But it's driving me insane

Verse 5:

Everything in the way is so shiny today

A queer and unusual fall

Spirals of golden haze, here and there in a blaze

Like beams of light in the storm

Maybe you were here and maybe you weren't

Maybe you touched somebody and got burnt

The silent sun has got me on the run

Burning a hole in my brain

I'm dreamin' of you, that's all I do

But it's driving me insane

RECORDED IN 1965
(OUTTAKE FROM *BRINGING IT ALL BACK HOME*)
FIRST RELEASED IN 1991 ON
**THE BOOTLEG SERIES, VOLS 1-3:
RARE & UNRELEASED 1961-1991**

An outtake from *Bringing It All Back Home*, 'Farewell, Angelina' was long assumed to be one of those Dylan-penned songs that he himself never recorded. Made familiar by Joan Baez's 1965 version and her frequent concert performances of it, the song's cast of colourful characters (cross-eyed pirates, a camouflaged parrot, little elves, gypsies, queens and knaves), although often edited down by Baez, still sounds like archetypal Dylan of the period. The song also somehow seems to demand its writer's husky delivery. A wonderful outtake, made on January 13, 1965, this was the only time Dylan recorded it. 'Farewell, Angelina' probably had its roots in a Scottish song from the 1850s, 'Farewell To Tarwathie' and as such would perhaps have made an appropriate addition to *Bringing It All Back Home*'s radical mix of acoustic folk and electric rock.

FAREWELL, ANGELINA

FAREWELL, ANGELINA

WORDS & MUSIC BY BOB DYLAN

tin - gles and the Trum - pets play slow
emp - ty___ By the edge___ of the sea___
deuce And the ace___ once ran wild

1-6.

Fare - well An - ge - li - na The sky is on fire___ And I___ must
Fare - well An - ge - li - na The sky is trem-bling And I___ must
Fare - well An - ge - li - na The sky is fold - ing___ I'll see you in a

7.

go.   2. There's_   But fare -
leave.   3. The
while.

Verse 4:
See the cross-eyed pirates sitting
Perched in the sun
Shooting tin cans
With a sawed-off shotgun
And the neighbors they clap
And they cheer with each blast
Farewell Angelina
The sky's changing colour
And I must leave fast

Verse 5:
King Kong, little elves
On the rooftops they dance
Valentino-type tangos
While the makeup man's hands
Shut the eyes of the dead
Not to embarrass anyone
Farewell Angelina
The sky is embarrassed
And I must be gone

Verse 6:
Instrumental

Verse 7:
The machine guns are roaring
The puppets heave rocks
The fiends nail time bombs
To the hands of the clocks
Call me any name you like
I will never deny it
Farewell Angelina
The sky is erupting
I must go where it's quiet

RECORDED IN 1983
(OUTTAKE FROM *INFIDELS*)
FIRST RELEASED IN 1991 ON
THE BOOTLEG SERIES, VOLS 1-3:
RARE & UNRELEASED 1961-1991

'Foot Of Pride', coming as it did during a period of rich outpourings from Dylan while he was preparing to make *Infidels*, is a complex and mature song that never made it onto the album. If its lyric is hard to decipher in detail, its broad message is unmistakable: 'Foot Of Pride' is a classic Dylan broadside against phonies, manipulators and demagogues. As such it relates to the withering protest songs of his youth, although it has an added dimension of spirituality and the ambivalent concept of eternal damnation. The song also recalls some of Dylan's earlier work in that the melody is stripped down and the tempo speeded up in order to make the music a bracing vehicle for the complex lyrics – think 'It's Alright, Ma (I'm Only Bleeding)' and 'Maggie's Farm'.

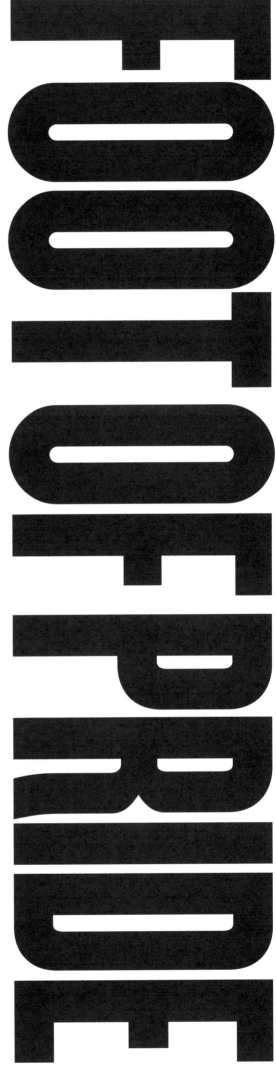

FOOT OF PRIDE

WORDS & MUSIC BY BOB DYLAN

B⁵

You know what they say a-bout be-in' nice to the right peo-ple
In these times of com-pas-sion when con-
feed you co-co-nut bread, spice

on the way up Soon-er or lat-er you gon-na meet them__ com-in'
-for-mi-ty's in fash-ion Say one more stu-pid thing to me be-fore the fi-nal nail is
buns in your bed If you don't mind sleep-in' with your head face down in a

B   G♯m

down
dri-ven in   Well, there ain't no go-in' back   When your
grave

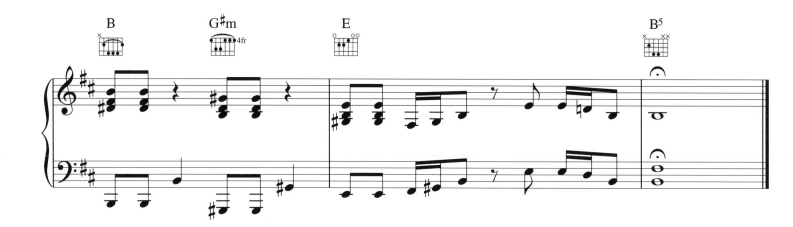

Verse 4:

Well, they'll choose a man for you to meet tonight
You'll play the fool and learn how to walk through doors
How to enter into the gates of paradise
No, how to carry a burden too heavy to be yours
Yeah, from the stage they'll be tryin' to get water outa rocks
A whore will pass the hat, collect a hundred grand and say thanks
They like to take all this money from sin, build big universities to study in
Sing "Amazing Grace" all the way to the Swiss banks

Well, there ain't no goin' back *etc.*

Verse 5:

They got some beautiful people out there, man
They can be a terror to your mind and show you how to hold your tongue
They got mystery written all over their forehead
They kill babies in the crib and say only the good die young
They don't believe in mercy
Judgement on them is something that you'll never see
They can exalt you up or bring you down main route
Turn you into anything that they want you to be

Well, there ain't no goin' back *etc.*

Verse 6:

Yes, I guess I loved him too
I can still see him in my mind climbin' that hill
Did he make it to the top, well he probably did and dropped
Struck down by the strength of the will
Ain't nothin' left here partner, just the dust of a plague
that has left this whole town afraid
From now on, this'll be where you're from
Let the dead bury the dead. Your time will come
Let hot iron blow as he raised the shade

Well, there ain't no goin' back *etc.*

GOLDEN LOOM

RECORDED IN 1975 (OUTTAKE FROM *DESIRE*)
FIRST RELEASED IN 1991 ON
**THE BOOTLEG SERIES, VOLS 1-3:
RARE & UNRELEASED 1961-1991**

This loping blues-flavoured song was a 1975 outtake from the *Desire* sessions which were, by all accounts, disorganised affairs. Among the last recorded songs intended for the album, 'Golden Loom' partly reflects the influence of Jacques Levy, who had co-written some of the other material for *Desire* (although this particular one is credited to Dylan alone). It is a mystical, dream-like song, a more fanciful and abstract relation of 'Isis', featuring a fisherman's daughter as an incarnation of female power and a weaver of human destinies. By the time of its recording at the end of July, the rolling assembly of guest musicians had landed on Scarlet Rivera, Rob Stoner, Howie Wyeth and Emmylou Harris. Not for the first time, it seems this outtake released on *The Bootleg Series, Vols 1-3* is a perhaps less-than-perfect performance of an interesting song that may have been jettisoned for nothing more than the want of a satisfactory take.

GOLDEN LOOM

WORDS & MUSIC BY BOB DYLAN

1. Smok-y au-tumn night,_

(3° Instrumental)

stars up___ in the sky___
(2.) near the im-mort-al___ shrine___

(4.) in the dis-mal light

2. First we wash our feet,
3° Instrumental
4. I walk a - cross the bridge

Page 69

RECORDED IN 1963
ORIGINALLY RELEASED IN 1963 ON
BROADSIDE BALLADS, VOL. 1
OFFICIALLY RELEASED IN 2010 ON
**THE BOOTLEG SERIES, VOL 9:
THE WITMARK DEMOS 1962-1964**

Written in 1962, 'John Brown' had to wait almost half a century for its official release. It returns us to Dylan's early anti-war protest period and is based on an old Irish folk tune. It tells an unvarnished tale of a prideful mother who sends her son off to war in a foreign country from which he returns injured and blind. Dylan's rough demo made for publisher M. Witmark & Sons in August 1963 is the version that eventually surfaced on *The Bootleg Series, Vol. 9*, although in the same year Dylan had sneaked out a pseudonymous performance of the song for an album titled *Broadside Ballads, Vol. 1* on which, for contractual reasons, he appeared as Blind Boy Grunt.

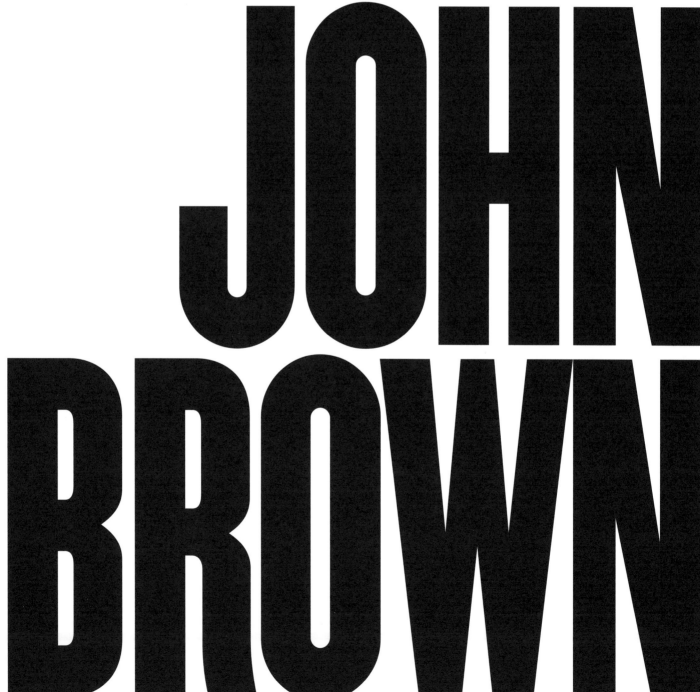

JOHN BROWN

JOHN BROWN

WORDS & MUSIC BY BOB DYLAN

Verse 4:
She got a letter once in a while and her face broke into a smile
As she showed them to the people from next door
And she bragged about her son with his uniform and gun
And these things you called a good old-fashioned war

Oh! Good old-fashioned war!

Verse 5:
Then the letters ceased to come, for a long time they did not come
They ceased to come for about ten months or more
Then a letter finally came saying, "Go down and meet the train
Your son's a-coming home from the war"

Verse 6:
She smiled and went right down, she looked everywhere around
But she could not see her soldier son in sight
But as all the people passed, she saw her son at last
When she did she could hardly believe her eyes

Verse 7:
Oh his face was all shot up and his hand was all blown off
And he wore a metal brace around his waist
He whispered kind of slow, in a voice she did not know
While she couldn't even recognize his face!

Oh! Lord! Recognize his face

Verse 8:
"Oh tell me, my darling son, pray tell me what they done
How is it you come to be this way?"
He tried his best to talk but his mouth could hardly move
And the mother had to turn her face away

Verse 9:
"Don't you remember, Ma, when I went off to war
You thought it was the best thing I could do?
I was on the battleground, you were home… acting proud
You wasn't there standing in my shoes"

Verse 10:
"Oh, and I thought when I was there, God, what am I doing here?
I'm a-tryin' to kill somebody or die tryin'
But the thing that scared me most was when my enemy came close
And I saw that his face looked just like mine"

Oh! Lord! Just like mine!

Verse 11:
"And I couldn't help but think, through the thunder rolling and stink
That I was just a puppet in a play
And through the roar and smoke, this string is finally broke
And a cannonball blew my eyes away"

Verse 12:
As he turned away to walk, his Ma was still in shock
At seein' the metal brace that helped him stand
But as he turned to go, he called his mother close
And he dropped his medals down into her hand

THE GROOM'S STILL WAITING AT THE ALTAR

RECORDED IN 1981
FIRST RELEASED IN 1981 AS A SINGLE

Recorded in Los Angeles in May 1981, 'The Groom's Still Waiting At The Altar' hailed from the *Shot Of Love* album sessions, although in retrospect some thought it anticipated the tougher sound of the next album, *Infidels*. Initially it was released only as a B-side to the 'Heart Of Mine' single but was later included on *Shot Of Love* CD releases dating from 1985. In any case, it recalls 'Leopard-Skin Pill-Box Hat' and other memorable Dylan electric blues songs from the mid-60s. A really strong track that received airplay in late 1981, 'The Groom's Still Waiting At The Altar' nonetheless attracted Dylan's vague disapproval at the time: 'I felt it was too rushed,' he said, 'I felt we'd lost the original riff… I listened back to it later, and it sounded okay, but it wasn't really the way I wanted to play it.'

THE GROOM'S STILL WAITING AT THE ALTAR

WORDS & MUSIC BY BOB DYLAN

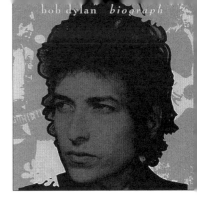

1. Prayed in the ghet-to   with my face in the ce-ment,
2. Try to be   pure at heart,   they ar-rest you for rob-bery,
(3.) know what I can say a-bout Claud-ette   that would-n't come back   to haunt me,

(Verses 4 & 5 see block lyrics)

East of the Jor - dan, hard__ as the Rock of Gib-ral - tar,
West of the Jor - dan, east__ of the Rock of Gib-ral - tar,
West of the Jor - dan, west__ of the Rock of Gib-ral - tar,

I see the burn - ing of the page,__ Cur - tain
I see the burn - ing of the stage,__ Cur - tain
I see the burn - ing of the cage,__ Cur - tain

ris - in' on a new age, See the groom still wait - in' at the al - tar.__
ris - in' on a new age, See the groom still wait - in' at the al - tar.__
ris - in' on a new stage, See the groom still wait - in' at the al - tar.__

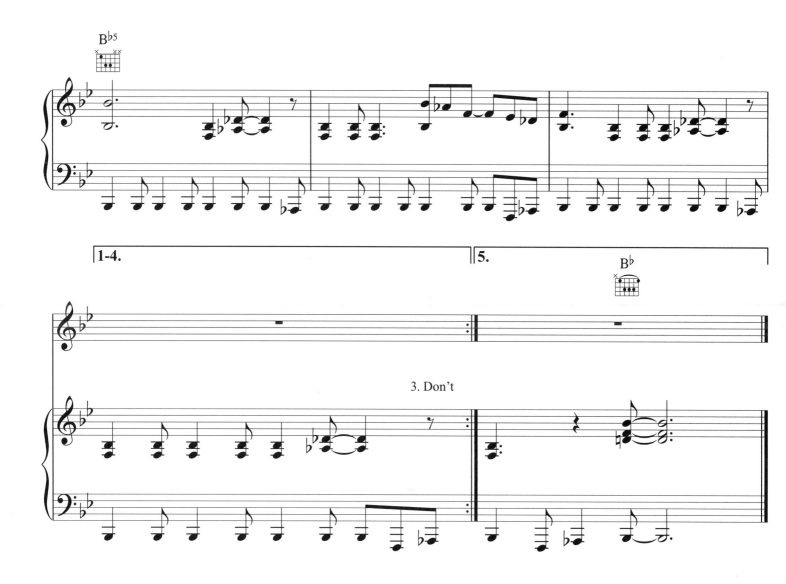

Verse 4:

Put your hand on my head, baby, do I have a temperature?

I see people who are supposed to know better standin' around like furniture

There's a wall between you and what you want and you got to leap it

Tonight you got the power to take it, tomorrow you won't have the power to keep it

West of the Jordan, east of the Rock of Gibraltar

I see the burning of the stage

Curtain risin' on a new age

See the groom still waitin' at the altar

Verse 5:

Cities on fire, phones out of order

They're killing nuns and soldiers, there's fighting on the border

What can I say about Claudette? Ain't seen her since January

She could be respectably married or running a whorehouse in Buenos Aires

West of the Jordan, east of the Rock of Gibraltar

I see the burning of the stage

Curtain risin' on a new age

See the groom still waitin' at the altar

HUCK'S TUNE

RECORDED IN 2007
FIRST RELEASED IN 2007 ON
LUCKY YOU SOUNDTRACK ALBUM

This song comes from the soundtrack of *Lucky You*, Curtis Hanson's 2007 drama set in the world of poker. By general assent, the movie seemed to have been enjoyed more by poker players than general audiences. Dylan's song namechecks Eric Bana's chancer hero Huck Cheever, who tries to win a tournament in Vegas, while conspicuously losing a battle with his personal problems. The song, like much of the film, is hardly upbeat: 'You think I'm blue, I think so too/In my words, you'll find no guile/The game's gotten old, the deck's gone cold/And I'm gonna have to put you down for a while'.

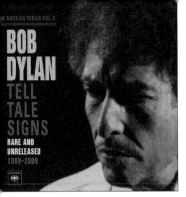

HUCK'S TUNE

WORDS & MUSIC BY BOB DYLAN

deck's gone cold__ I'm gon-na have to put you down for a while.__

Verse 2:
Every day we meet on any old street
And you're in your girlish prime
The short and the tall are coming to the ball
I go there all the time
Behind every tree there's something to see
The river is wider than a mile
I tried you twice, you can't be nice
I'm gonna have to put you down for a while

Verse 3:
Here come the nurse with money in her purse
Here come the ladies and men
You push it all in and you've no chance to win
You play 'em on down to the end
I'm laying in the sand gettin' a sunshine tan
Movin along, riding in style
From my toes to my head you knock me dead
I'm gonna have to put you down for a while

Verse 4:
I count the years and I shed no tears
I'm blinded to what might have been
Nature's voice makes my heart rejoice
Play me the wild song of the wind
I found hopeless love in the room above
When the sun and the weather were mild
You're as fine as wine, I ain't handing you no line
I'm gonna have to put you down for a while

Verse 5:
All the merry little elves can go hang themselves
My faith is as cold as can be
I'm stacked high to the roof and I'm not without proof
If you don't believe me, come see
You think I'm blue? I think so too
In my words you'll find no guile
The game's gotten old, the deck's gone cold
And I'm gonna have to put you down for a while

IF YOU GOTTA GO, GO NOW, GO NOW (OR ELSE YOU YOU GOT TO STAY ALL NIGHT)

RECORDED IN 1965
(OUTTAKE FROM *BRINGING IT ALL BACK HOME*)
FIRST RELEASED IN 1991 ON
**THE BOOTLEG SERIES, VOLS 1-3:
RARE & UNRELEASED 1961-1991**

A terrific pop song, 'If You Gotta Go, Go Now' did little for British group Liverpool Five who released it first in the US in July 1965. It became a hit in the UK when Manfred Mann covered it in September of the same year. Dylan himself recorded various versions in January 1965, out of which came two takes: one was released in the Netherlands as a single and the other, identified as an outtake from the *Bringing It All Back Home* album, was shelved until 1991 when it appeared on *The Bootleg Series, Vols 1-3*. This is the version presented here. The Netherlands single did not chart, but the song travelled well enough in Europe. French rocker Johnny Hallyday did well with a version in French, 'Maintenant Ou Jamais', and Fairport Convention enjoyed their only UK chart hit with a more literal French language version titled 'Si Tu Dois Partir'. Ricky Nelson, Cowboy Junkies and The Flying Burrito Brothers also recorded the song.

IF YOU GOTTA GO, GO NOW
(OR ELSE YOU GOT TO STAY ALL NIGHT)

WORDS & MUSIC BY BOB DYLAN

Moderately ♩ = 134

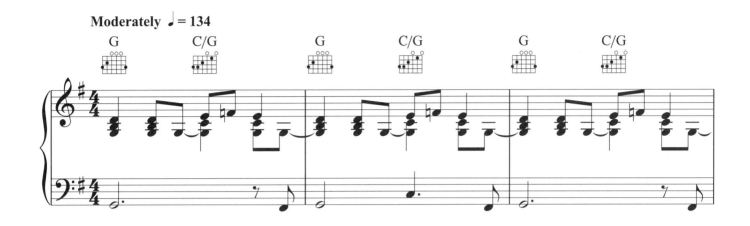

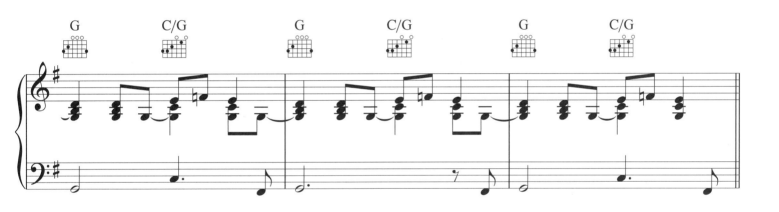

1. Lis - ten to____ me, ba - by   There's some - thing you must see____
2. It ain't that____ I'm ques - tion - in' you   To take part in a - ny quiz____

else you got-ta stay all night._____

else you got to stay all night._____

I'LL KEEP IT WITH MINE

RECORDED IN 1965
(OUTTAKE FROM *BRINGING IT ALL BACK HOME*)
FIRST RELEASED IN 1985 ON
BIOGRAPH

This strangely beguiling song never made it onto a studio album although it first popped up on bootlegs in the mid-1960s in the form of the 1964 piano-and-vocal demo Dylan made for music publishers M. Witmark & Sons. This demo received no 'official bootleg' release until 2010, when The Witmark Demos formed Volume 9 of *The Bootleg Series*. A second piano-and-vocal recording was made on January 14, 1965 during sessions for the *Bringing It All Back Home* album and this version was eventually released 20 years later on Dylan's three-volume *Biograph* retrospective. A slightly ragged rehearsal of the song, this time with a full band, was recorded on January 27, 1966 during sessions for *Blonde On Blonde*. This track was finally released on *The Bootleg Series, Vols 1-3*. Arrangements of the second and third versions mentioned above are represented here. Given his repeated essays on what many fans believe to be a first-rate song, it is odd that Dylan never really felt sufficiently comfortable with it to put it on an album. 'Maybe it didn't sound like a record to me,' he has said, 'but if people like it, they like it.'

I'LL KEEP IT WITH MINE

WORDS & MUSIC BY BOB DYLAN

1. You will
search, babe   At   a - ny   cost
(2.) help   it   If_____ you   might   think   I'm_____ odd
(3.) train   leaves   At   half   past   ten

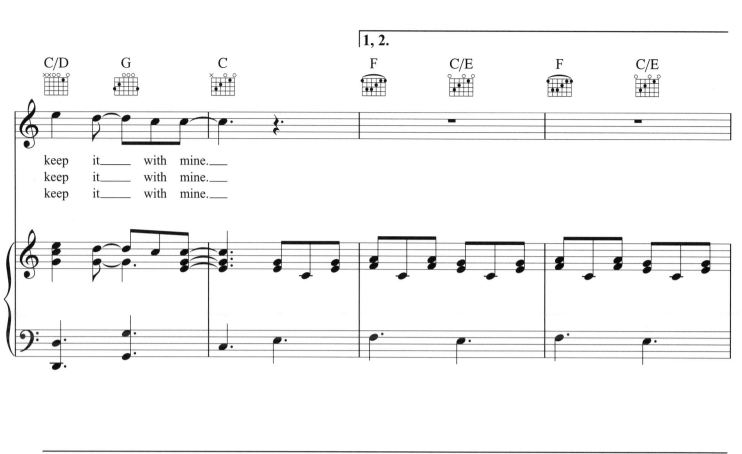

keep it_____ with mine.___
keep it_____ with mine.___
keep it_____ with mine.___

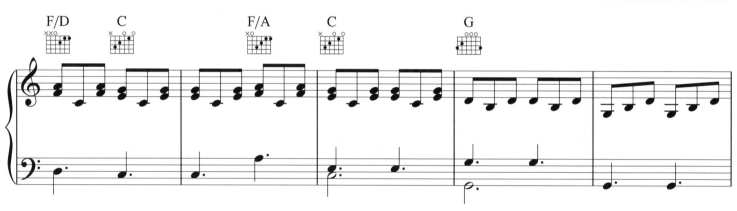

2. I_____ can't
3. The_____

RECORDED IN 1963
FIRST RELEASED IN 1985 ON
BIOGRAPH

Dylan probably said all that needs to be said about this heartfelt 1963 acoustic song in the note to it included in *Biograph*, where it first appeared: 'I wrote that on the West Coast at Joan Baez's house... I had heard a Scottish ballad on an old 78 record that I was really trying to capture the feeling of, that was haunting me... There were no lyrics or anything, it was just a melody, had bagpipes and a lot of stuff in it. I wanted lyrics that would feel the same way... I don't remember what the original record was.' A likely contender is 'The Water Is Wide', an old Scottish tune that exists in many variant versions and is melodically similar to Dylan's song, albeit with a slightly different metre.

LAY DOWN YOUR WEARY TUNE

LAY DOWN YOUR WEARY TUNE

WORDS & MUSIC BY BOB DYLAN

Additional lyrics:

The last of leaves fell from the trees
And clung to a new love's breast
The branches bare like a banjo played
To the winds that listened best

I gazed down in the river's mirror
And watched its winding strum
The water smooth ran like a hymn
And like a harp did hum

Lay down your weary tune, lay down
Lay down the song you strum
And rest yourself 'neath the strength of strings
No voice can hope to hum

RECORDED IN 1964
(OUTTAKE FROM *ANOTHER SIDE OF BOB DYLAN*)
FIRST RELEASED IN 1991 ON
THE BOOTLEG SERIES, VOLS 1-3:
RARE & UNRELEASED 1961-1991

This fine song shows Dylan articulating gentle regret at a lost love. There is no irony, hostility or jealousy in the lyric and the melody perfectly matches the spirit of the words. Joan Baez covered it as 'Daddy, You Been On My Mind' in 1965, but the perky rhythm of her rendition feels very different to Dylan's slower, more deliberate and heartfelt version. This was an outtake from the *Another Side* sessions recorded in June 1964 and it easily stands comparison with the very strong songs finally selected for the album.

MAMA, YOU BEEN ON MY MIND

MAMA, YOU BEEN ON MY MIND

WORDS & MUSIC BY BOB DYLAN

1. Per - haps it's the col-or of the
(2.) don't mean trou-ble, please don't put me down___
(3.) though my mind is ha-zy an' my thoughts_
(Verses 4-6 see block lyrics)

sun cut flat___ An' cov'-rin' the cross-roads I'm stand-ing at___
___ or get up-set I___ am not plead-ing or say-in', "I___ can't for-get"
___ they might be nar-row Where you been___ don't both-er me_ nor bring me___ down_ in sor-row

Or may-be it's the wea-ther or some-thing like that But
I do not walk the floor bowed down an' bent, but yet
It don't e -ven mat-ter___ to me where you're wak - in' up to-mor - row But

Verse 4:

I am not askin' you to say words like "yes" or "no"
Please understand me, I got no place for you t' go
I'm just breathin' to myself, pretendin' not that I don't know
Mama, you been on my mind

Verse 5:
Instrumental

Verse 6:

When you wake up in the mornin', baby, look inside your mirror
You know I won't be next to you, you know I won't be near
I'd just be curious to know if you can see yourself as clear
As someone who has had you on his mind

RED RIVER SHORE

RECORDED IN 1997
(OUTTAKE FROM *TIME OUT OF MIND*)
FIRST RELEASED IN 2008 ON
THE BOOTLEG SERIES, VOL. 8: TELL TALE SIGNS

One of Dylan's great skills has been to expound a long narrative using a very simple repetitive melody. He did it triumphantly in 'Lily, Rosemary And The Jack Of Hearts' and in 'Isis'. 'Red River Shore', recorded in January 1997 in the *Time Out Of Mind* sessions, certainly has a strong repetitive melody but the lyric wavers uncertainly between the literal and the mystical. Perhaps Dylan realised this, because 'Red River Shore' never made the final cut. Even so, it remains a strangely compelling song and was included on *The Bootleg Series, Vol. 8*.

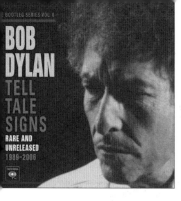

RED RIVER SHORE

WORDS & MUSIC BY BOB DYLAN

1. Some of us turn off the lights_ and we lay   up in the moon-light shoot-ing by,_
(2.) sat   by her side   and for a while   I tried   to   make that girl_ my wife,_
(3.) knew when I first   laid eyes   on her   I could nev - er be_ free,_
   (Verses 4-8 see block lyrics)

some of us   scare our - selves_ to death___ in the dark
she   gave me her best   ad - vice_____ and she   said
one_ look at her_ and I   knew right a - way

from the Red Riv-er___ shore.___

girl from the Red Riv-er___ shore.___

from the Red Riv-er___ shore.

2. Well, I

3. Well, I

Page 110

Verse 4:
Well, I'm wearing the cloak of misery
And I've tasted jilted love
And the frozen smile upon my face
Fits me like a glove
Well, I can't escape from the memory
Of the one I'll always adore
All those nights when I lay in the arms
Of the girl from the Red River shore

Verse 5:
Well, we're living in the shadows of a fading past
Trapped in the fires of time
I've tried not to ever hurt anybody
And to stay out of the life of crime
And when it's all been said and done
I never did know the score
One more day is another day away
From the girl from the Red River shore

Verse 6:
Well, I'm a stranger here in a strange land
But I know this is where I belong
I'll ramble and gamble for the one I love
And the hills will give me a song
Though nothing looks familiar to me
I know I've stayed here before
Once a thousand nights ago
With the girl from the Red River shore

Verse 7:
Well, I went back to see about her once
Went back to straighten it out
Everybody that I talked to had seen us there
Said they didn't know who I was talking about
Well the sun went down a long time ago
And doesn't seem to shine anymore
I wish I could have spent every hour of my life
With the girl from the Red River shore

Verse 8:
Now I heard a guy who lived a long time ago
A man full of sorrow and strife
That if someone around him died and was dead
He knew how to bring him on back to life
Well, I don't know what kind of language he used
Or if they do that kind of thing anymore
Sometimes I think nobody ever saw me here at all
Except the girl from the Red River shore

RECORDED IN 1963
(OUTTAKE FROM *THE TIMES THEY ARE A-CHANGIN'*)
FIRST RELEASED IN 1991 ON
**THE BOOTLEG SERIES, VOLS 1-3:
RARE & UNRELEASED 1961-1991**

This early Dylan song sees him firmly in Woody Guthrie mode. By the summer of 1963 when he considered it for possible inclusion on *The Times They Are A-Changin'*, 'Paths Of Victory' had undergone several changes since he first started working on it in 1962. In March 1963 it had taken firmer shape for a performance on a folk music special sponsored by The Westinghouse Broadcasting Company. This version, complete with sprightly piano, comes from the *Times They Are A-Changin'* sessions of mid-1963. It reveals 'Paths Of Victory' to be unlike most of Dylan's other protest songs of the time, eschewing real-life cases of social injustice (Hollis Brown, Hattie Carroll, Medgar Evers) in favour of almost abstract evangelical imagery: 'Trails of troubles /Roads of battles /Paths of victory / I shall walk.'

PATHS OF VICTORY

PATHS OF VICTORY

WORDS & MUSIC BY BOB DYLAN

1. The trail_____ is dus - ty And my road_
(2.) walked to the riv - er I
(3.) eve - nin'___ dusk was roll - in' I was
(Verses 4-6 see block lyrics)

___ it might be rough___ But the bet - ter roads are wait - in'
turned my head up___ high___ I saw that sil - ver lin -
walk - ing down___ the track___ There was a one - way wind a - blow-

Paths of vic - t'ry___ We shall walk.___

Verse 4:
The gravel road is bumpy
It's a hard road to ride
But there's a clearer road a-waitin'
With the cinders on the side

Trails of troubles *etc.*

Verse 5:
That evening train was rollin'
The hummin' of its wheels
My eyes they saw a better day
As I looked across the fields

Trails of troubles *etc.*

Verse 6:
The trail is dusty
The road it might be rough
But the good road is a-waitin'
And boys it ain't far off

Trails of troubles *etc.*

NOBODY 'CEPT YOU

RECORDED IN 1973
(OUTTAKE FROM *PLANET WAVES*)
FIRST RELEASED IN 1991 ON
THE BOOTLEG SERIES, VOLS 1-3:
RARE & UNRELEASED 1961-1991

'Nobody 'Cept You', recorded in November 1973, could arguably have been the best song on *Planet Waves*, but Dylan rejected it at the last minute in favour of 'Wedding Song'. The recorded version that eventually appeared on *The Bootleg Series, Vols 1-3* is a little ragged around the edges and it is possible that the lack of an acceptable take contributed to its eventual omission from the studio album. Even so, a *Planet Waves* version of the song had been eagerly anticipated by some who had seen Dylan perform an acoustic version during the early stages of a 1974 tour with The Band. It was not to be and 'Nobody 'Cept You' stands as evidence of Dylan's willingness to move on from a song, rather than dwell on it, when something else fired his imagination.

NOBODY 'CEPT YOU

WORDS & MUSIC BY BOB DYLAN

1. There's no-thing 'round here I be-lieve_
2. No-thing 'round here I care to try___

_ in   'Cept you,_____   yeah_
_ for   'Cept you,_____   yeah_

you_____   to me that's
Got no-thing left   to live or
No-thing_ much mat-ters or seems to please_

And there's no-thing

RECORDED IN 1962
(OUTTAKE FROM *THE FREEWHEELIN' BOB DYLAN*)
FIRST RELEASED IN 1991 ON
**THE BOOTLEG SERIES, VOLS 1-3:
RARE & UNRELEASED 1961-1991**

This song came very close to being included on *The Freewheelin' Bob Dylan*. Actually present on a few test pressings, it was at the last minute omitted in favour of 'A Hard Rain's A-Gonna Fall'. Both are protest songs addressing the threat of war, but they take subtly different perspectives. If 'A Hard Rain's A-Gonna Fall' revolves around its recurring image of nuclear fallout, 'Let Me Die In My Footsteps' suggests a different kind of fatalism. Constructing underground bomb shelters – all the rage in the nervy 1960s – speaks of a particularly forlorn brand of despair. Here Dylan's message is, if the end is nigh, at least stay above ground and enjoy life while you can: 'Let me die in my footsteps / Before I go down under the ground.' There is little doubt that this anthemic song meant a lot to Dylan since he uncharacteristically supplied his own quite lengthy note to it when it was still being mooted for inclusion on *Freewheelin'*. It remains very much part of his 60s radical songwriting and, although he performed it live many times in the early days, by the time he was making demos for publisher M. Witmark & Sons as early as 1962, he stopped recording this particular song after 1 minute 20 seconds, questioning whether it should be included. 'It's awful long,' he explains.

LET ME DIE IN MY FOOTSTEPS

LET ME DIE IN MY FOOTSTEPS

WORDS & MUSIC BY BOB DYLAN

go down un-der___ the ground.___

2. There's been
3. I don't

you go down un-der___ the ground.___

Verse 4:

There's always been people that have to cause fear
They've been talking about a war now for many long years
I have read all their statements and I've not said a word
But now Lawd God, let my poor voice be heard
Let me die in my footsteos
Before I go down under the ground

Verse 5:

If I had rubies and riches and crowns
I'd buy the whole world and change things around
I'd throw all the guns and the tanks in the sea
For they are mistakes of a past history
Let me die in my footsteps
Before I go down under the ground

Verse 6:

Let me drink from the waters where the mountain streams flood
Let the smell of wildflowers flow free through my blood
Let me sleep in your meadows with the green grassy leaves
Let me walk down the highway with my brother in peace
Let me die in my footsteps
Before I go down under the ground

Verse 7:

Go out in your country where the land meets the sun
See the craters and the canyons where the waterfalls run
Nevada, New Mexico, Arizona, Idaho
Let every state in this union seep down deep in your souls
And you'll die in your footsteps
Before you go down under the ground

RECORDED 1965
(OUTTAKE FROM *OH MERCY*) FIRST RELEASED IN
1991 ON
THE BOOTLEG SERIES VOLUMES 1-3

It remains something of a mystery why
'Series Of Dreams' never appeared on *Oh
Mercy*, Dylan's 26th studio album. Recorded
in New Orleans on 23 March 1989 for that
album, omitted and subsequently overdubbed
for a single release and inclusion in the 1991
three-volume launch of *The Bootleg Series*, it
appears to be one of those songs that tested
the mercurial relationship between Dylan and
producer Daniel Lanois. Lanois loved it but
Dylan had his reservations, particularly since
he felt Lanois preferred the bridge section to
the main melody. Characteristically unpre-
pared to overthink and rework, Dylan shelved
it. Subsequent critical opinion leaned towards
the view that 'Series Of Dreams' was a very
strong song and one that would have been
perfectly suited to *Oh Mercy*, an album widely
seen as a return to form for Dylan after the
relatively fallow period that followed 1976's
magnificent *Desire*.

SERIES OF DREAMS

SERIES OF DREAMS

WORDS & MUSIC BY BOB DYLAN

think-ing of a-ny-thing___ spe - ci-fic
-ing a-ny great con-nec - tion
-ing for a-ny spe-cial as - sist - ance

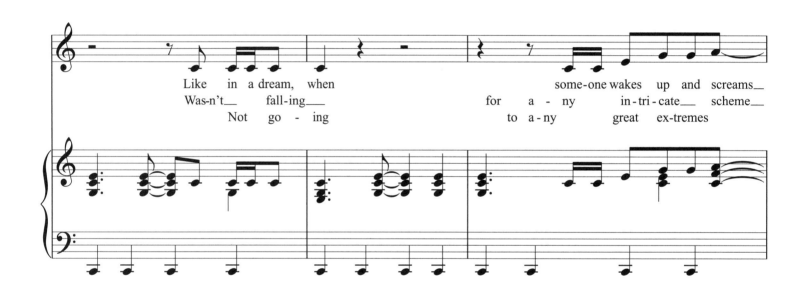

Like in a dream, when some-one wakes up and screams___
Was-n't___ fall-ing___ for a-ny in-tri-cate___ scheme___
Not go - ing to a-ny great ex-tremes

___ No-thing too ve-ry sci - en - ti - fic___
___ No - thing that would pass in - spec - tion
___ I'd al-rea-dy gone the dis -

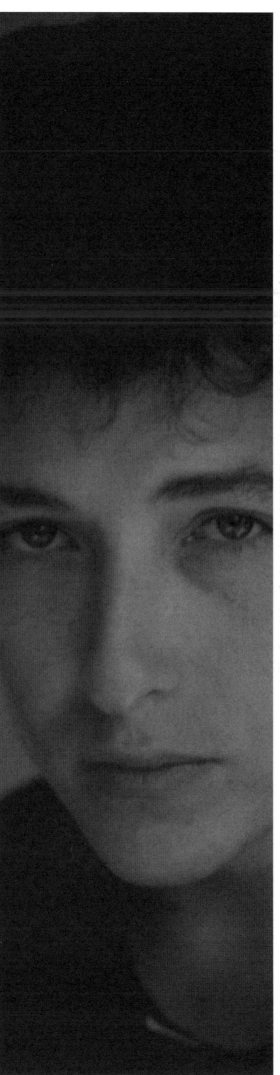

TELL ME, MOMMA

RECORDED IN 1966
(LIVE RECORDING, MANCHESTER, UK)
FIRST RELEASED IN 1998 ON
THE BOOTLEG SERIES, VOL. 4: BOB DYLAN LIVE 1966

From the so-called 'Royal Albert Hall' concert, 'Tell Me, Momma' launched the amplified second half of a 1966 tour set that was to assume legendary status. Although that tour did conclude with two shows at London's Royal Albert Hall, its UK leg had previously taken place in both Sheffield and Manchester and the best tapes were judged to be those made at Manchester's Free Trade Hall. Dated May 17, 1966, they were used for Columbia's live recording but may have been mislabelled as 'The Royal Albert Hall Concert'. It was, in fact, in Manchester that they were made and where Dylan was audibly accused of being a 'Judas' by an audience member for forsaking his folk roots. This alleged dereliction of duty was heightened by Dylan's decision to make the first half of the show acoustic and the second electric. Clearly annoyed at the heckler, Dylan urged his musicians, The Hawks (soon to be rechristened The Band), to crank up the volume. It resulted in a performance that was both defiant and extremely loud. The performance of 'Tell Me, Momma' was also shot by D. A. Pennebaker for a shaky documentary of the tour titled *Eat the Document*. The song's inherent interest will perhaps always be overshadowed by its historical context in the Dylan legend.

TELL ME, MOMMA

WORDS & MUSIC BY BOB DYLAN

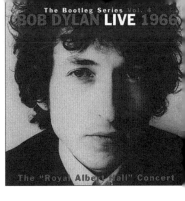

1. Ol' black Bas - com,___ don't break no mirrors
(Verses 2 & 3 see block lyrics)

Cold black wa - ter dog,___ make no tears___

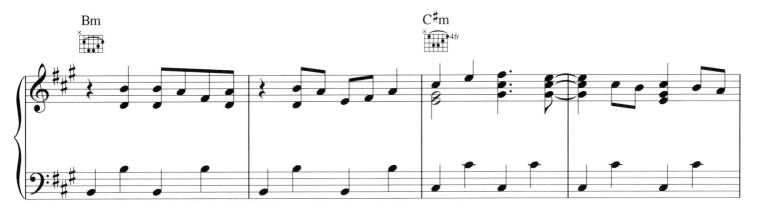

Ooh

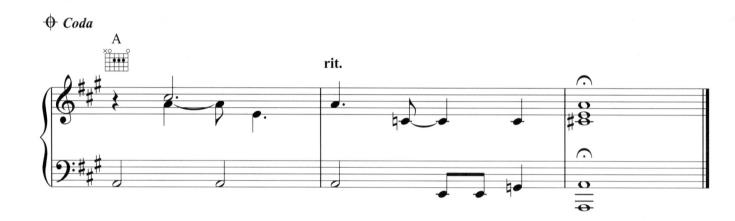

Verse 2:

Hey, John, come and get me some candy goods
Shucks, it sure feels like it's in the woods
Spend some time on your January trips
You got tombstone moose up and your grave-yard whips
If you're anxious to find out when your friendship's gonna end
Come on, baby, I'm your friend!
And I know that you know that I know that you show
Something is tearing up your mind

Tell me, momma *etc.*

Verse 3:

Ooh, we bone the editor, can't get read
But his painted sled, instead it's a bed
Yes, I see you on your window ledge
But I can't tell just how far away you are from the edge
And, anyway, you're just gonna make people jump and roar
Watcha wanna go and do that for?
For I know that you know that I know that you know
Something is tearing up your mind

Ah, tell me, momma *etc.*

PERCY'S SONG

RECORDED IN 1963
FIRST RELEASED IN 1985 ON
BIOGRAPH

A staple of the youthful Bob Dylan's concert sets, 'Percy's Song' was recorded in New York City in October 1963. Never included on any official album until *Biograph* (1985), for some Dylan fans it had been a standout track on an early unofficial bootleg that surfaced in the late 60s and early 70s. Its familiarity was enhanced when Joan Baez performed a hotel room extract from it in the 1965 cult Dylan documentary *Don't Look Back*, and it was perhaps the most melodic of Dylan's several 'first person' or 'character' songs that include 'Dink's Song' (the lament of a suicidal unwed mother) and 'Ballad Of Donald White' (about a lifelong social misfit condemned to death). Dylan credits the melody line of 'Percy's Song' to his 60s friend and contemporary Paul Clayton, but the lyric's outrage at a 99-year custodial sentence handed down for man-slaughter after a road accident, is pure young Dylan, protest singer.

PERCY'S SONG

WORDS & MUSIC BY BOB DYLAN

Verses 4-20 see block lyrics

one of your friends   Is   in   trou - ble deep
Jo - li - et   pri - son   And nine-ty-nine__ years
Man - slaugh-ter   In the high - est of de - gree,__

Turn,   turn_____   to the rain_____   And the wind.
Turn,   turn_____   to the rain_____   And the wind.
Turn,   turn_____   to the rain_____   And the wind.

1-19.   20.

3. Oh

Verse 4:
I sat down and wrote
The best words I could write
Turn, turn, turn again
Explaining to the judge
I'd be there on Wednesday night
Turn, turn to the rain
And the wind

Verse 5:
Without a reply
I left by the moon
Turn, turn, turn again
And was in his chambers
By the next afternoon
Turn, turn to the rain
And the wind

Verse 6:
Instrumental

Verse 7:
Could ya tell me the facts?
I said without fear
Turn, turn, turn again
That a friend of mine
Would get ninety-nine years
Turn, turn to the rain
And the wind

Verse 8:
A crash on the highway
Flew the car to a field
Turn, turn, turn again
There was four persons killed
And he was at the wheel
Turn, turn to the rain
And the wind

Verse 9:
But I knew him as good
As I'm knowin' myself
Turn, turn, turn again
And he wouldn't harm a life
That belonged to someone else
Turn, turn to the rain
And the wind

Verse 10:
The judge spoke
Out of the side of his mouth
Turn, turn, turn again
Sayin', "The witness who saw
He left little doubt"
Turn, turn to the rain
And the wind

Verse 11:
That may be true
He's got a sentence to serve
Turn, turn, turn again
But ninety-nine years
He just don't deserve
Turn, turn to the rain
And the wind

Verse 12:
Too late, too late
For his case it is sealed
Turn, turn, turn again
His sentence is passed
And it cannot be repealed
Turn, turn to the rain
And the wind

Verse 13:
But he ain't no criminal
And his crime it is none
Turn, turn, turn again
What happened to him
Could happen to anyone
Turn, turn to the rain
And the wind

Verse 14:
Instrumental

Verse 15:
And at that the judge jerked forward
And his face it did freeze
Turn, turn, turn again
Sayin', "Could you kindly leave
My office now, please"
Turn, turn to the rain
And the wind

Verse 16:
Well his eyes looked funny
And I stood up so slow
Turn, turn, turn again
With no other choice
Except for to go
Turn, turn to the rain
And the wind

Verse 17:
I walked down the hallway
And I heard his door slam
Turn, turn, turn again
I walked down the courthouse stairs
And I did not understand
Turn, turn to the rain
And the wind

Verse 18:
Instrumental

Verse 19:
And I played my guitar
Through the night to the day
Turn, turn, turn again
And the only tune
My guitar could play
Was, "Oh the Cruel Rain
And the Wind"

Verse 20:
Instrumental

RECORDED IN 1976
(LIVE PERFORMANCE, TAMPA, FLORIDA)
FIRST RELEASED IN 1991 ON
**THE BOOTLEG SERIES, VOLS 1-3:
RARE & UNRELEASED 1961-1991**

Dylan never recorded 'Seven Days' in a studio and performed it live only five times, during the second *Rolling Thunder Revue* tour in April 1976. He offered it to Eric Clapton, who did not take him up on it, although also present at the Malibu studios at the time was Ronnie Wood, who did, subsequently featuring it on his album *Gimme Some Neck*. This arrangement is based on Dylan's *Rolling Thunder* performance in Tampa, Florida and reveals 'Seven Days' to be an edgy variation on the Johnny Cash 'Train Of Love' metaphor. Here, the narrator fixates on the week (interestingly expressed as seven days 'connected') he must wait before his long-gone 'beautiful comrade from the north' arrives in town.

SEVEN DAYS

SEVEN DAYS

WORDS & MUSIC BY BOB DYLAN

1. Se-ven days,

(2.)

(3.)

sev-en more days she'll be com-in' I'll be
ev-er since I been a child Ev-er since
I been good while I been wait-in' May-be

waiting___ at the sta-tion   for   her to ar-rive_____
___ I seen her smile,   I   ain't for-got - ten her eyes_____
guil-ty of hes-it-at - in',   I   just been hold-in'___ on_____

Sev-en more days,   all___ I got-ta do is sur-vive._____
She had a face_ could out-shine the   sun in the skies._____
Sev-en more days,   and all that - 'll be gone._____

1, 2.   **3.**

2. She been gone_
3. I been good_   There's

D.S. al Coda

There's

Coda

Page 150

WALKIN' DOWN THE LINE

RECORDED IN 1963
(PUBLISHING DEMO FOR M. WITMARK & SONS
PUBLISHING COMPANY)
FIRST RELEASED IN 1991 ON
THE BOOTLEG SERIES, VOLS 1-3:
RARE & UNRELEASED 1961-1991

This jaunty song with its repetitive hook
was first recorded by Dylan in 1962 for
Broadside magazine, giving them a basis for
transcription to enable publication of the
music. That newly-founded, inexpensively-
produced but highly influential music magazine took the contemporary folk revival very
seriously, often hosting heated debates
about what constituted genuine folk music.
It was therefore ironic that Dylan's 'Walkin'
Down The Line' would soon be recorded by
pop artists Jackie DeShannon, Ricky Nelson
and Glen Campbell. Establishing Dylan as a
songwriter for other artists was the sole
purpose of the demos he made for music
publishers M. Witmark & Sons. 'Walkin'
Down The Line', recorded for them in 1963,
was one of the first of many: an impressive
237 Dylan songs were published by 1966.

WALKIN' DOWN THE LINE

WORDS & MUSIC BY BOB DYLAN

1. I got a hea - vy - head - ed gal
2. My mon - ey comes and goes___
3. I see the morn - ing light___
(*Verse 4 see block lyrics*)

Verse 4:

I got my walkin' shoes
I got my walkin' shoes
I got my walkin' shoes
An' I ain't a-gonna lose
I believe I got the walkin' blues

RECORDED IN 1974
FIRST RELEASED IN 1985 ON
BIOGRAPH

Of all the Dylan outtakes, the superb 'Up To Me' is, at first hearing, one of the most inexplicable omissions. The album it was omitted from perhaps offers a clue: 1974's *Blood On The Tracks* already contains an embarrassment of riches, but 'Up To Me' remains an excellent performance of a finely constructed song. Possibly its resemblance to 'Shelter From The Storm' counted against it, perhaps so too did the unmistakeably personalised lyric. 'Shelter From The Storm' told a more generalised story, but 'Up To Me' includes the lines: 'And if we never meet again, baby, remember me / How my lone guitar played sweet for you that old-time melody / And the harmonica around my neck, I blew it for you, free / No one else could play that tune, you know it was up to me.'

UP TO ME

UP TO ME

WORDS & MUSIC BY BOB DYLAN

© COPYRIGHT 1974, RENEWED 2002 RAM'S HORN MUSIC.
ALL RIGHTS RESERVED. INTERNATIONAL COPYRIGHT SECURED.

Slight shuffle ♩ = 86

1. Ev-'ry-thing went from bad to worse, mon-ey nev-er changed a thing
(2.) thought a-bout it I nev-er would've done it, I guess I would've let it slide If I'd
3. U-nion Cen-tral is pull-in' out and the or-chids are in bloom
(Verses 4-12 see block lyrics)

Death kept fol-low-in', track-in' us down, at least I heard your blue-bird sing
lived my life by what oth-ers were think-in', the heart in-side me would've died I was
I've on-ly got me one good shirt left and it smells of stale per-fume In four-

Now some-bo-dy's got to show their hand, time is an en-e-my
just too stub-born to ev-er be gov-erned by en-forced in-sa-ni-ty
-teen months I've on-ly smiled once and I did-n't do it con-scious-ly

Verse 4:
It was like a revelation when you betrayed me with your touch
I'd just about convinced myself that nothin' had changed that much
The old Rounder in the iron mask slipped me the master key
Somebody had to unlock your heart, he said it was up to me

Verse 5:
Well, I watched you slowly disappear down into the officers' club
I would've followed you in the door but I didn't have a ticket stub
So I waited all night 'til the break of day, hopin' one of us could get free
When the dawn came over the river bridge, I knew it was up to me

Verse 6:
Oh, the only decent thing I did when I worked as a postal clerk
Was to haul your picture down off the wall near the cage where I used to work
Was I a fool or not to try to protect your identity?
You looked a little burned out, my friend, I thought it might be up to me

Verse 7:
Well, I met somebody face to face and I had to remove my hat
She's everything I need and love but I can't be swayed by that
It frightens me, the awful truth of how sweet life can be
But she ain't a-gonna make me move, I guess it must be up to me

Verse 8:
We heard the Sermon on the Mount and I knew it was too complex
It didn't amount to anything more than what the broken glass reflects
When you bite off more than you can chew you pay the penalty
Somebody's got to tell the tale, I guess it must be up to me

Verse 9:
Well, Dupree came in pimpin' tonight to the Thunderbird Café
Crystal wanted to talk to him, I had to look the other way
Well, I just can't rest without you, love, I need your company
But you ain't a-gonna cross the line, I guess it must be up to me

Verse 10:
There's a note left in the bottle, you can give it to Estelle
She's the one you been wond'rin' about, but there's really nothin' much to tell
We both heard voices for a while, now the rest is history
Somebody's got to cry some tears, I guess it must be up to me

Verse 11:
So go on, boys, and play your hands, life is a pantomime
The ringleaders from the county seat say you don't have all that much time
And the girl with me behind the shades, she ain't my property
One of us has got to hit the road, I guess it must be up to me

Verse 12:
And if we never meet again, baby, remember me
How my lone guitar played sweet for you that old-time melody
And the harmonica around my neck, I blew it for you, free
No one else could play that tune, you know it was up to me

TELL OL' BILL

RECORDED IN 2005
FIRST RELEASED IN 2005 ON
THE NORTH COUNTRY SOUNDTRACK ALBUM

This long song plays over the end titles of
North Country, Niki Caro's worthy 2005
film celebrating a legal breakthrough for
the women who won the first major
successful sexual harassment case in the
United States in 1984. One of three film
songs included on Volume 8 of *The Bootleg
Series*, 'Tell Ol' Bill' neither comments
literally on the movie plot nor does what
'Knockin' On Heaven's Door' did so
effectively for *Pat Garrett and Billy the Kid*
in creating a powerful emotional mood for a
particular scene. Even so, it is an interesting
addition to Dylan's occasional ventures
into writing film songs.

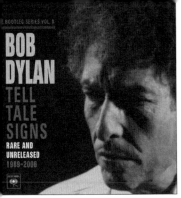

TELL OL' BILL

WORDS & MUSIC BY BOB DYLAN

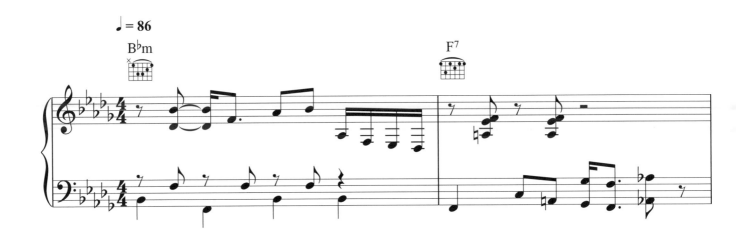

1. The riv-er   whis-pers   in   my ear_____
2. Tell   me straight out,   if   you will_____
3. I   walk   by tran-quil lakes_ and__ streams___
(Verse 4 see block lyrics)

I've hard-ly a pen-ny to my name____
Why must you____ tor-ture me____ with - in?____
As each____ new sea-son's dawn____ a - waits_____

The hea-ven's nev - er seemed____ so near____
Why must you come from your high hill
I lay a-wake at night with trou-bled dreams____

And all my bo-dy glows____ with flame.____
And throw my fate____ to the clouds and wind?____
The en - em - y____ is at the gate.____

Ly - ing rest-less in a hea - vy bed.
I've no-thing more to tell___ you now.___
Be - neath_ the gray_ and storm-y___ sky.___

Verse 4:

The evening sun is settin' low
The woods are dark, the town is too
They'll drag you down, they'll run the show
Ain't no telling what they'll do

Tell Ol' Bill when he comes home
That anything is worth a try
Tell him that I'm not alone
And the hour has come to do or die

All the world I would defy
Let me make it plain as day
I look at you now and I sigh
How could it be any other way?

QUINN THE ESKIMO (THE MIGHTY QUINN)

RECORDED IN 1967
FIRST RELEASED IN 1985 ON
BIOGRAPH

Earnest Dylan lyric interpreters have
always had their work cut out with 'Quinn
The Eskimo'. Dylan is the first to admit that
the song's UK chart success for the band
Manfred Mann in the summer of 1969
surprised him. 'I don't know what it was
about,' he said, 'I guess it was some kind of
nursery rhyme.' It seems most probable that
Dylan had recalled the lead performance in
Nicholas Ray's 1960 Inuit movie *The Savage
Innocents*. Here, some four years before he
became Zorba the Greek, Mexican-Irish
actor Anthony Quinn played Inuk the
Eskimo and so perhaps inspired a snappy
lyrical hook for what turned out to be one of
Dylan's most successfully covered songs.

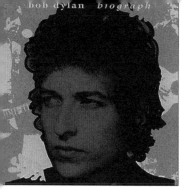

QUINN THE ESKIMO (THE MIGHTY QUINN)

WORDS & MUSIC BY BOB DYLAN

RECORDED IN 1971
FIRST RELEASED IN 1991 ON
**THE BOOTLEG SERIES, VOLS 1-3:
RARE & UNRELEASED 1961-1991**

Dylan wrote and recorded this engaging, country-flavoured waltz on November 4, 1971 at Blue Rock Studios, New York. It would take 20 years for his version to be released, on *The Bootleg Series, Vols 1-3*. An alternate take later appeared on *The Bootleg Series, Vol. 10: Another Self Portrait* but in the interim 'Wallflower' proved popular with other artists. Doug Sahm's version came first, in late 1972, with Dylan supplying backing vocals that were mixed into such prominence that he sounded like the lead singer. Buddy and Julie Miller made a spirited country version and Diana Krall named a 2015 album after the song, which she gives a slow, reflective treatment. It is interesting that Dylan's empathetic lyric for partner-less dancers everywhere was written during a period he later described as 'the worst time of my life' when he had returned to New York for the wrong reasons, finding there neither much of his past nor any obvious clues about his immediate future.

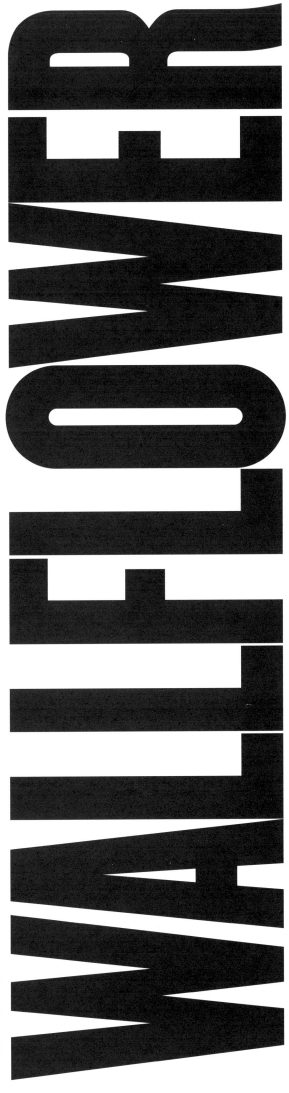

WALLFLOWER

WORDS & MUSIC BY BOB DYLAN

Original key F♯ major.

-flow - er, wall - flow - er Won't you dance with me?

RECORDED IN 1963
(OUTTAKE FROM *THE FREEWHEELIN' BOB DYLAN*)
FIRST RELEASED IN 1991 ON
**THE BOOTLEG SERIES, VOLS 1-3:
RARE & UNRELEASED 1961-1991**

Destined never to be released during the radical protest period that spawned it, Dylan's vivid portrait of a juvenile detention centre in his native state of Minnesota failed to make the final cut for either *The Free-wheelin' Bob Dylan* or *The Times They Are A-Changin'*. An outtake from the *Free-wheelin'* session recorded in April of 1963, 'Walls Of Red Wing' finally made it onto *The Bootleg Series, Vols 1-3*, revealing it to be an impassioned song whose lyric evoked an un-remittingly bleak institution for 12- to 17-year-old boys. It comes as little surprise that this is not one of the Dylan songs snapped up by acts like Peter, Paul and Mary, although Joan Baez did rise to the challenge.

WALLS OF RED WING

WALLS OF RED WING

WORDS & MUSIC BY BOB DYLAN

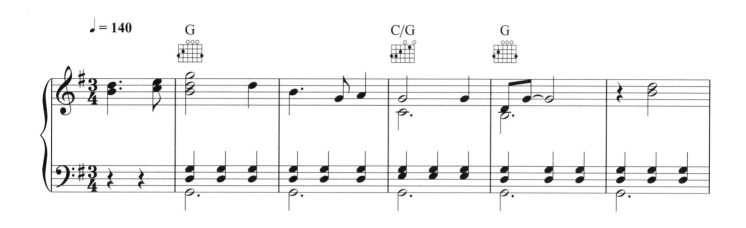

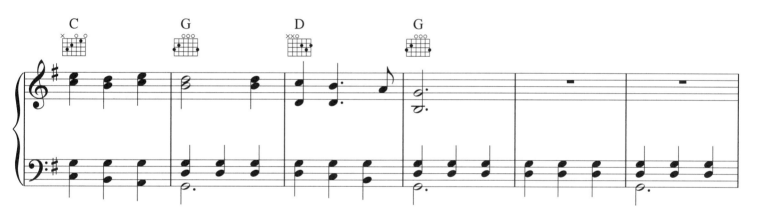

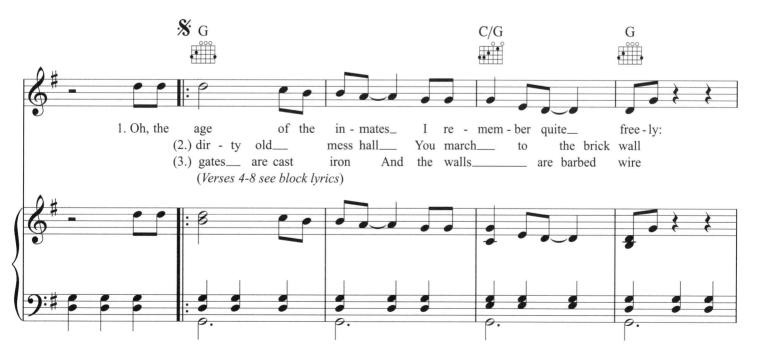

1. Oh, the age of the in-mates I re-mem-ber quite free-ly:

(2.) dir-ty old mess hall You march to the brick wall

(3.) gates are cast iron And the walls are barbed wire

(Verses 4-8 see block lyrics)

2. From the
3. Oh, the

D.S. al Coda

8. Oh,

Coda

walls   of   Red__   Wing.

rit.

Verse 4:
Oh, it's fare thee well
To the deep hollow dungeon
Farewell to the boardwalk
That takes you to the screen
And farewell to the minutes
They threaten you with it
Inside the walls
The walls of Red Wing

Verse 5:
It's many a guard
That stands around smilin'
Holdin' his club
Like he was a king
Hopin' to get you
Behind a wood pilin'
Inside the walls
The walls of Red Wing

Verse 6:
The night aimed shadows
Through the crossbar windows
And the wind punched hard
To make the wall-siding sing
It's many a night
I pretended to be a-sleepin'
Inside the walls
The walls of Red Wing

Verse 7:
As the rain rattled heavy
On the bunkhouse shingles
And the sounds in the night
They made my ears ring
'Til the keys of the guards
Clicked the tune of the morning
Inside the walls
The walls of Red Wing

Verse 8:
Oh, some of us'll end up
In St. Cloud Prison
And some of us'll wind up
To be lawyers and things
And some of us'll stand up
To meet you on your crossroads
From inside the walls
The walls of Red Wing

SHE'S YOUR LOVER NOW

RECORDED IN 1966
(OUTTAKE FROM *BLONDE ON BLONDE*)
FIRST RELEASED IN 1991 ON
**THE BOOTLEG SERIES, VOLS 1-3:
RARE & UNRELEASED 1961-1991**

Two versions of this outtake from *Blonde On Blonde* were recorded in New York in January 1966, one piano and vocal and one full band version featuring The Hawks (soon to become The Band). The complex lyric addresses the eternal triangle: in this case the narrator, his ex and her new boyfriend. With a running time of over six minutes and a mix of emotional stances it must have been challenging to sing, and in the outtake included on *The Bootleg Series, Vols 1-3* Dylan stumbles a little over the final lines. That was Take 19 and judged the best of 21 takes, after which 'She's Your Lover Now' was abandoned for good, leaving us without a finished version of what some believe to be one of Dylan's best songs.

SHE'S YOUR LOVER NOW

WORDS & MUSIC BY BOB DYLAN

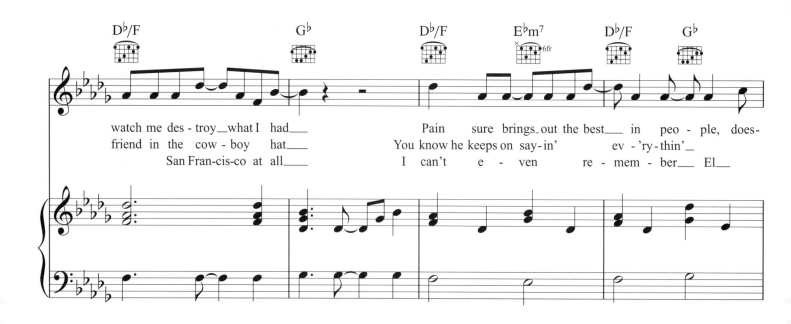

watch me des - troy__ what I had__
friend in the cow - boy hat__
San Fran-cis-co at all__
Pain sure brings__ out the best__ in peo - ple, does-
You know he keeps on say-in' ev - 'ry-thin'__
I can't e - ven re - mem - ber__ El__

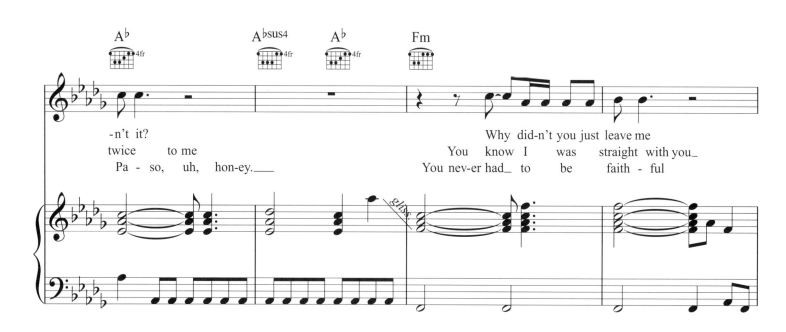

-n't it?
twice to me
Pa - so, uh, hon-ey.__
Why did-n't you just leave me
You know I was straight with you__
You nev-er had__ to be faith - ful

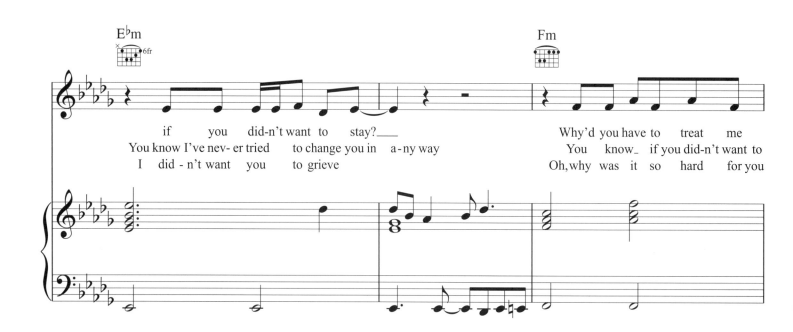

if you did-n't want to stay?__
You know I've nev - er tried to change you in a-ny way
I did - n't want you to grieve
Why'd you have to treat me
You know__ if you did-n't want to
Oh, why was it so hard for you

so bad?   Did it have   to   be   that   way?_____

be   with me__ That   you   could...   did-n't have   to stay_____

If you did - n't want to   be with me,   just to   leave?_____

Now   you   stand   here   ex - pect-in' me_____ to re - mem - ber some-thin' you for-got to

Now   you   stand here say-in' you for - give   and   for - get._____   Hon - ey, what   can I

Now   you   stand here while   your   fin - ger's_   go - in'___   up my__

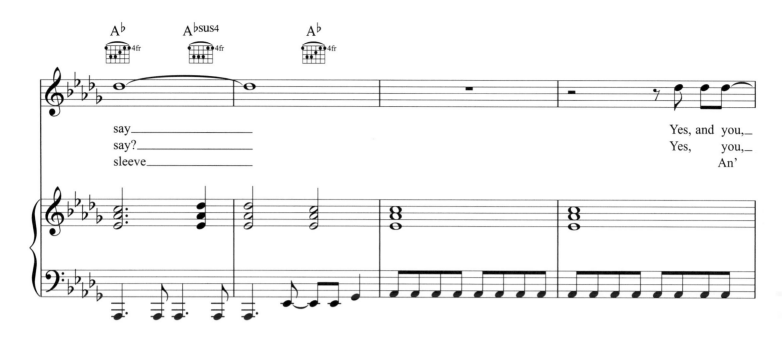

say_____
say?_____
sleeve_____

Yes, and you,__
Yes, you,__
An'

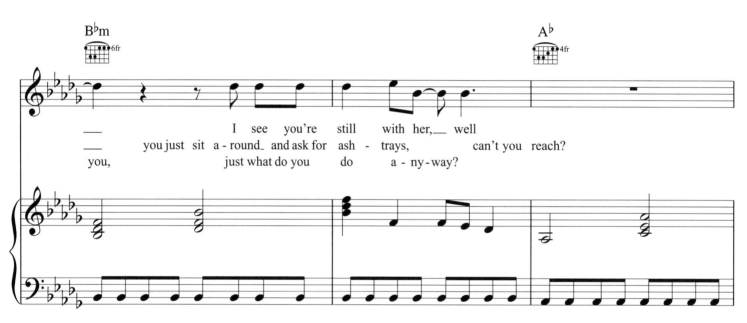

__ I see you're still with her,__ well
__ you just sit a - round__ and ask for ash - trays, can't you reach?
you, just what do you do a - ny - way?

That's fine 'cause she's com - in' on__ so strange, can't you
I see you kiss her on the cheek ev - 'ry - time__ she gives a speech
Ain't there no - thin' you can say?

WATCHING THE RIVER FLOW

RECORDED IN 1971
FIRST RELEASED IN 1971 AS A SINGLE AND ON
BOB DYLAN'S GREATEST HITS VOLUME II

Recorded at the same Blue Rock Studios sessions as 'When I Paint My Masterpiece', 'Watching The River Flow' differed structurally in that the song was built by Dylan on top of a basic blues rock track that had emerged from studio jam sessions featuring producer Leon Russell on piano and Jesse Ed Davis on guitar. The song's lyric has been interpreted as revealing Dylan in meditative mood in the spring of 1971, undecided on his next career move and, for the time being, just content to watch the scenery go by. This needs to be balanced against the fact that he is alleged to have written both the melody and the lyrics in ten minutes at the end of the session, which is not to say that he didn't have the song's contemplative sentiment at the back of his mind already, just that the prime catalyst was that underlying power-house blues-rock track. Backed with 'Spanish Is The Loving Tongue', the song was chosen to be released as a single on 3 June 1971 and then included on *Bob Dylan's Greatest Hits Volume II* five months later.

WATCHING THE RIVER FLOW

WORDS & MUSIC BY BOB DYLAN

1. What's the mat-ter with me_
2. Wish I was back in the ci-ty

I don't have much to say
In-stead of this old bank of sand,

With the

sit down on this bank of sand
right now___ I'll just sit here so con-ten-ted-ly

And___ watch___ the riv-er flow.
And watch the

riv-er flow.___

Peo - ple dis - a - gree - ing on all just a - bout a - ny - thing, yeah
Peo - ple dis - a - gree - ing ev' - ry - where you look___
Makes you wan - na

Makes you stop and all won - der why
Why
stop and read a book
Why

on - ly yes - ter - day___ I saw some - bo - dy on the street Who just could - n't help
on - ly yes - ter - day___ I saw some - bo - dy on the street That was

but cry
Oh,_____ this
real - ly shook
But_____ this

ol' riv - er keeps on roll - in', though___

No mat - ter what gets in the way and which way the wind does blow

And as long as it does I'll___ just sit here___ And watch the

riv - er flow.___

WHEN I PAINT MY MASTERPIECE

RECORDED IN 1971
DEMO VERSION FIRST RELEASED IN 2013 ON
**THE BOOTLEG SERIES, VOL. 10:
ANOTHER SELF PORTRAIT**

A thought-provoking tour of Europe provides the backdrop to 'When I Paint My Masterpiece', which was written and recorded by Dylan in 1971. His version made its debut on *Bob Dylan's Greatest Hits Volume II*. By then, however, the song had already appeared on the album *Cahoots* by Dylan's *Basement Tapes* collaborators, The Hawks, aka The Band. Leon Russell produced Dylan's version at Blue Rock Studios in New York City, and presumably also provided the piano accompaniment on the demo version, which was finally released in 2013 on *The Bootleg Series Vol. 10*. This version forms the basis of the arrangement in this collection.

WHEN I PAINT MY MASTERPIECE

WORDS & MUSIC BY BOB DYLAN

♩ = 72

1. Oh, the streets of
Rome are filled with rub-ble An-cient foot-prints are ev-'ry-where_
(2.) spent in-side the Co - li-se - um Dodg-ing li - ons and wast-in'time
(3.) Rome and land-ed in Brus-sels On a plane ride_ so bum-py that I al-most cried_

You can al-most think that you're see - in' dou-ble On a
Oh, those might-y kings of the jun-gle, I could hard-ly stand_ to see 'em
Cler-gy-men in u-ni-form and young girls pull-in' mus-cles

Sail - in' round_ the world_ in a dir - ty gon - do - la

Sure wish I had - n't a sold_____ my old Vic - trol - la

INDEX OF FIRST LINES

RECOMMENDED FOR YOU...

AM1008271

AM1012055

AM995060

AM1008326

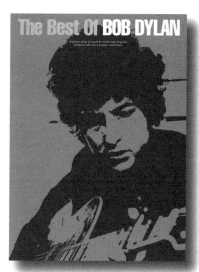

AM950060

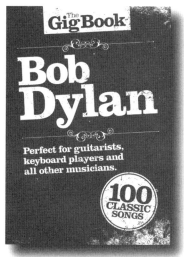

AM997304

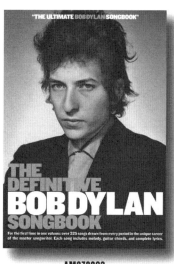

AM978923

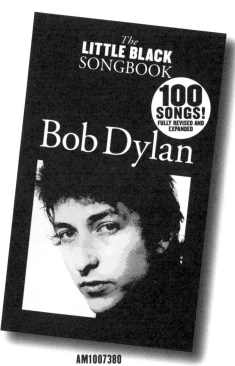

AM1007380

ALSO AVAILABLE ONLINE AND FROM ALL GOOD MUSIC SHOPS...

Adele: 25
ORDER NO. AM1009712

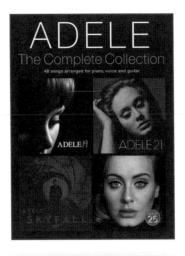

Adele: The Complete Collection
ORDER NO. AM1011802

Coldplay: A Head Full Of Dreams
ORDER NO. AM1011516

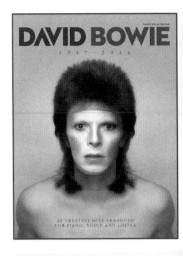

David Bowie 1947 - 2016
ORDER NO. AM1011670

Hits Of The Year 2016
ORDER NO. AM1012330

Fifty Years Of Hits: Volume One
ORDER NO. AM1012143

The Top Ten Love Songs To Play On Piano
ORDER NO. AM1012275

The Top Ten Piano Songs Of All Time
ORDER NO. AM1012242

The Top Ten Most Beautiful Pieces To Play On Piano
ORDER NO. AM1012253

Really Easy Piano Playalong: Chart Hits
ORDER NO. AM1010647

Now That's What I Call Christmas
ORDER NO. AM1012561

Now That's What I Call Music! 95
ORDER NO. AM1012572

 # LOOK OUT FOR MORE TITLES IN THE NOW! MUSIC RANGE

Just visit your local music shop and ask to see our
huge range of music in print.
www.musicsales.com